CONTENTS

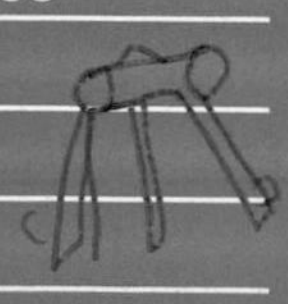

STAR WARS™

Published by Pedigree Books Limited,
Beech Hill House, Walnut Gardens, Exeter, Devon EX4 4DH. Published 2008.

photograph album

ANAKIN SKYWALKER >>>

As a young man, Anakin Skywalker was headstrong and confident, with a loving and generous heart. However, a darker side began to emerge within him that he found difficult to control.

<<< OBI-WAN KENOBI

After the tragic events surrounding the end of the Clone Wars, Obi-Wan chose to live as a hermit on Tatooine. For many years his home was a one-room hut between the western Dune Sea and the Jundland Wastes.

MASTER YODA >>>

The oldest member of the Jedi Council, Master Yoda was an expert in Form IV lightsaber combat nd a wise and cautious Jedi Master. Many of the ublic's greatest Jedi trained under Yoda when ere children.

<<< PADMÉ AMIDALA

As wise as she was beautiful, Padmé joined the Apprentice Legislature at the age of eleven and was elected Queen of Naboo at the age of fourteen. However, all her self-discipline could not prevent her from falling in love with her Jedi protector, Anakin Skywalker.

PRINCESS LEIA >>>

Unaware of her true heritage, Princess Leia grew up as the daughter of the Viceroy of the planet Alderaan, Bail Organa. She was always a bit of a tomboy, but she was enmeshed in the world of politics and became the youngest Senator in galactic history.

<<< LUKE SKYWALKER

Raised on a farm by his aunt and uncle, Luke Skywalker thought he was the son of a spice freighter navigator. He longed to enter the Academy and become a pilot. But not even his protective uncle could keep him from his true destiny.

HAN SOLO >>>

Born on Corellia, Han's earliest memory was of begging on the streets. He enrolled in the Imperial Academy, but his stubborn nature and belief in fairness led to him being discharged. He became a smuggler, and was arrogant, charming and impulsive.

<<< DARTH VADER

After the Clone Wars, Darth Vader helped Emperor Palpatine hunt down and exterminate nearly all the remaining Jedi Knights, caring nothing that they had once been his friends and colleagues.

MESSAGE RECORDING 5469

NAME: QUI-GON JINN

LOCATION: NABOO STARSHIP HEADING TOWARDS TATOOINE

The ever-greedy Trade Federation had stopped all shipping to the small planet of Naboo by putting a blockade of starships around the planet. Supreme Chancellor Valorum sent my young Padawan, Obi-Wan Kenobi, and me to settle the conflict.

Obi-Wan and I boarded the Trade Federation starship, and Obi-Wan had a bad feeling, although I admit that I didn't sense anything wrong at first. However, moments after I had advised Obi-Wan not to centre on his anxiety, the Republic cruiser that carried us here was destroyed! We leapt up and drew our lightsabers. The door soon slid open and a group of battle droids peered in, their weapons cocked. Our lightsabers made short work of many of them, creating a shower of sparks and metal parts. Obi-Wan used the Force to send several more crashing into the wall. Then we hurried to the bridge door and began to cut through it, knowing that Nute Gunray and his cowardly colleagues were behind it. Almost immediately, we sensed destroyer droids rolling towards us. As Obi-Wan pointed out in his usual wry manner, it was clear that the mission was way past the negotiation stage!

We dashed away from the laser attack and went up the ventilation shaft, emerging in a giant hangar bay. Thousands of battle droids were loading onto landing craft – it was an invisible army! I simply cannot understand why the Trade Federation would make such a bold move, but one thing was clear – we had to get down to Naboo and contact Supreme Chancellor Valorum. We agreed to stow aboard separate ships and meet down on the planet – that would give us the best chance of success.

I reached the planet's surface at twilight, and monstrous MTTs (Multi Troop Transports) were soon emerging from the mist. All sorts of creatures fled from them at top speed, and as I ran, a strange, brainless creature by the name of Jar Jar Binks grabbed hold of me and we barely escaped being crushed by a transport.

As I was trying to persuade Jar Jar that he didn't owe me a life debt, two STAPs (Single Trooper Aerial Platform) burst out of the mist at high speed, chasing my young Padawan. I flung Jar Jar down into the mud as the troops fired laser bolts at Obi-Wan and deflected the bolts back at the STAPs; they blew up. Yet again, Obi-Wan had forgotten to turn his weapon's power off, and the water had fried it. It won't take long to recharge, but hopefully he has learned his lesson this time!

Jar Jar Binks turned out to be more helpful than we had first thought. He is a Gungan, and he offered to take us to his underwater city of Otoh Gunga. He warned us that he had been banished and in any case, Gungans were not fond of outsiders, but at that moment anything seemed better than coming face-to-blaster with a thousand battle droids. We put on our breathing masks and followed the Gungan down into the murky depths of the lake.

Eventually we saw Otoh Gunga in the distance – a strange, glowing habitat made up of large bubbles. As soon as we entered the city, we faced four armed guards and their lethal electro-poles. Jar Jar was clearly as unwelcome as we were. We were taken to see Boss Nass, the Gungan leader.

MESSAGE RECORDING 5471

NAME: JAR JAR BINKS

LOCATION: NABOO STARSHIP HEADING TOWARDS TATOOINE

Oyi, mesa no wanten go back home – mesa knowen what mesa in for, but tis demunded byda guds. Tis una live debett. Soon as mesa back, mesa put in chains. Master Qui-Gon tryen talken witda Boss Nass, but Gungans no liken outlaunders! Master Qui-Gon un Obi-Wan muy muy talken on da Gungans un da Naboo maken symbiont circle. Mesa no understun, nor Boss Nass. He say wesa no caren abouda Naboo. Hesa gibben dem una bongo – un say da speedest way tooda Naboo tis goen through da core. Dose Jedi sure not knowen everythen. Mesa told dem hesa setten dem up. Goen through da planet core is bad bombin!

Den Master Qui-Gon tellen Boss Nass bouten da live debett un sayen he wanten una navigator. Mesa not believen hearen! Better dead in Otoh Gunga dan deader in da core!

Mesa nebber say mesa maxibig navigator – not mesa fault wesa almost fish food! When wesa attacked by da opee! Mesa got so skeered, mesa steer us unto its mouth. Ooops! But wesa got free unda opee crunched up by una suno aqua monstair. Den wesa havin una very skeery close-up witda colo claw fish, juss as da bongo losen power un starten sink'n. Mesa panic – monstairs out der, leak'n inside, all'n sink'n and no power!

Master Qui-Gon putten his han on mesa shoulder un mesa feelen maxibig sleepy. When mesa waken, wesa back on da surface – un oie boie, wesa die'n – wesa go'n tip over una waterfall! Mesa think'n desa Jedi is no berry safen! But desa guys bombad un wesa escapen un creep'n unto Theed.

Queen Amidala of da Naboo march'n off to una detention camp, witda ooder girls un guards. Jedi rescuen un escapen in da transports. Sure, der plenty Naboo bongos in da hangar, but der also more-n fifty battlen droids. Alarms starten scream-scream un mesa knowen mean'n – maxibig trouble comen desa way!

Obi-Wan free-en da pilots un Master Qui-Gon cutten da guards down bombad, un wesa race-n on board una ship. Den wesa escapen!

Mesa met una Naboo girl Padmé. Shesa una Queen's girl. Berry nice. Da hyperdrive leak'n, so wesa lan on una planet Tatooine for fuel un repair. Da generator is kaput – wesa needen una new one. Master Qui-Gon, hesa headen for da city Mos Espa, togedder witda R2-D2 astro droid un Padmé un mesa. Mesa juss knowen dis starten maxibig more trouble!

MESSAGE RECORDING 5489

NAME: ANAKIN SKYWALKER

LOCATION: NABOO STARSHIP HEADING TOWARDS CORUSCANT

My life has changed so much in the last couple of days. One minute I was just like any other slave boy (except I was a better pilot!) and the next I was meeting an angel and Jedi Knights and getting my whole world turned upside down!

It all started when old Watto called me in to watch the shop while he did some selling. There was a group of people in the shop, and Watto took the man and the droid off with him, leaving two others with me. One of them was a peculiar creature called Jar Jar, but the other was the most beautiful person I have ever seen in my whole life. I think she must be an angel, and her name is Padmé.

The strangers wanted a generator, and of course Watto was trying to fleece them. After they left the shop, a sandstorm blew up, so of course I couldn't leave them outside. Sandstorms are very, very dangerous. Mom gave them shelter and food in our little house, and we got talking. I showed Padmé See-Threepio. I think she was impressed that I could build a droid!

Master Qui-Gon is a Jedi, and their ship had broken down during a very important mission to Coruscant. They had no money to pay Watto, and without the parts, they wouldn't be able to repair the ship. Well, obviously I had to help! I said I would enter the Podrace. Mom didn't like it – she says that she dies every time Watto makes me race – but I love it, and the prize money would pay for the parts they needed!

It was the most exciting race I have ever been in. I felt as if everything depended on winning – and I couldn't bear to lose in front of Padmé! Sebulba played his usual dirty tricks and there were a few worrying moments, but something kept me calm and focused, and I won! I had never felt so good in all my life.

Winning was good enough for me – I never dreamed that anything more would come of it. But then Master Qui-Gon told me that I was free – part of the deal with Watto was that I would no longer be a slave if I won. I have the chance to make all my dreams come true. I am going to travel with the Jedi to Coruscant, and see if the Jedi Council will accept me for training. Master Qui-Gon says that I am strong with the Force. But I had to leave Mom behind.

At first I didn't want to leave her, but something inside me was telling me it was the right thing to do. Maybe it was the Force that Master Qui-Gon talks about so much. I said goodbye to See-Threepio and to my friends. But the hardest thing was saying goodbye to Mom. It was even harder than the time I climbed the great dune to chase the banthas away so they wouldn't be shot. But she wants me to go; she wants me to have this chance. And one day, when I am a Jedi, I will come back and free her. I promised her that.

As we ran across the desert to join the ship, we were attacked by a dark-cloaked figure on a speeder bike. He had a double-bladed lightsaber! I raced to the ship and we took off, flying low over the small cloud of dust that was Master Qui-Gon and the mysterious warrior. They leaped over each other in an incredible display of acrobatics and fighting. Then we lowered the ramp and Qui-Gon jumped on to it, closely followed by the stranger. I could see him properly now – his face was a mass of red and black tattoos. Master Qui-Gon knocked him off the ramp and we rocketed away.

MESSAGE RECORDING 5495

NAME: OBI-WAN KENOBI

LOCATION: CORUSCANT

At long last we arrived back on Coruscant. We were met by Supreme Chancellor Valorum and Senator Palpatine, the Naboo representative. Queen Amidala and her retinue went off with Senator Palpatine, together with Jar Jar and Anakin. My Master and I stayed with the Supreme Chancellor. We had to speak to the Jedi Council as soon as possible.

As soon as we stood before the twelve Jedi of the Council, my Master told them about his mysterious attacker and declared that he believed it had been a Sith Lord. Master Ki-Adi Mundi was quick to remind us that the Sith have been extinct for a millennium, but Master Yoda seemed deeply disturbed. He reminded us that the dark side is hard to see, and the Council agreed that the attacker would probably try again. They instructed us to stay with the Naboo Queen and protect her.

At that point I turned to leave, but to my surprise my Master told the Council about young Anakin, saying that he believes he is the Chosen One of the prophecy – the one who will bring balance to the Force. He asked that Anakin be trained as a Jedi!

The Council seemed impressed – my Master's opinion is highly respected-- and they agreed to see Anakin. But I knew that the boy could not pass their tests – he is far too old! I begged my Master not to defy the Council again. He could

be sitting on the Council himself if he would just follow the code. My pleas fell on deaf ears – Master Qui-Gon simply told me that I still have much to learn.

Meanwhile, there have been long and serious discussions between Senator Palpatine and Queen Amidala. It is true that the Republic is not what it once was. The Senate is full of squabbling delegates and Supreme Chancellor Valorum seems incapable of taking control. Although he has been Naboo's strongest supporter, Queen Amidala has moved for a vote of no confidence in him. With him in charge, there is little chance that the Senate would act on the invasion, and Naboo has to be her priority.

The Council saw and tested Anakin, and as I expected they have refused to train him as a Jedi. Master Mace Windu said that there is too much anger in him, and Master Yoda said that the boy's future is clouded. However, my Master announced that he would take Anakin on as his Padawan learner. This came as a bit of a shock to me! A Jedi Master can only have one apprentice at a time, so I told the Council that I am ready to face the trials to become a Jedi Knight, but Master Yoda said that I have more to learn.

Queen Amidala has decided to return to Naboo while the Senate votes for a new Supreme Chancellor. This could draw out the Queen's attacker, so Master Qui-Gon and I are going to accompany her and discover the identity of the dark warrior. The Council has agreed to let Anakin travel with us.

The boy is dangerous – the whole Council senses it. Why can't my Master see it too?

MESSAGE RECORDING 5506

NAME: PADMÉ AMIDALA

LOCATION: NABOO

We have arrived on Naboo and I immediately sent Jar Jar on a mission to the Gungan city. We have no army – our only hope is to persuade the Gungans to join forces with us. I hope that I can be more persuasive than Master Qui-Gon was in Otoh Gunga!

Although I have been preoccupied with the terrible danger to my home planet, I have also been thinking about little Anakin and the strange position in which he now finds himself. There is something about him that is so endearing – he is so honest and kind.

The journey to Naboo has given us all the chance to think, and Obi-Wan has apologised to Master Qui-Gon. It is not his place to disagree with him about Anakin. Obi-Wan is just grateful that his Master thinks he is ready for the trials.

Jar Jar persuaded Boss Nass to meet me, and I revealed my true identity to him. Poor Anakin could hardly believe it when he realised that the girl in the royal robes was only a decoy, and his friend Padmé was the true Queen of Naboo! Of course, Master Qui-Gon and Obi-Wan had sensed the truth almost immediately, but like all Jedi, they are very discreet.

Thankfully, Boss Nass had the wisdom to understand that the time has come to join forces. Otherwise, both our societies will be lost forever. Preparations have begun in earnest. The Trade Federation army is much larger and stronger than we thought. The battle will be a diversion – the Gungans must draw the droid army away from the cities, while I and my followers enter the city using secret passages that only we Naboo know. When we reach the main entrance, Captain Panaka will create a diversion and we will enter the palace and capture the Viceroy.

Master Qui-Gon is concerned about the Gungans – many of them could be killed. My plan is to send what pilots I can to knock out the droid control ship above the planet. Without communications, the droids will be helpless. There are so many dangers and many things that can go wrong with these plans. Everything depends on me and my team reaching the Viceroy.

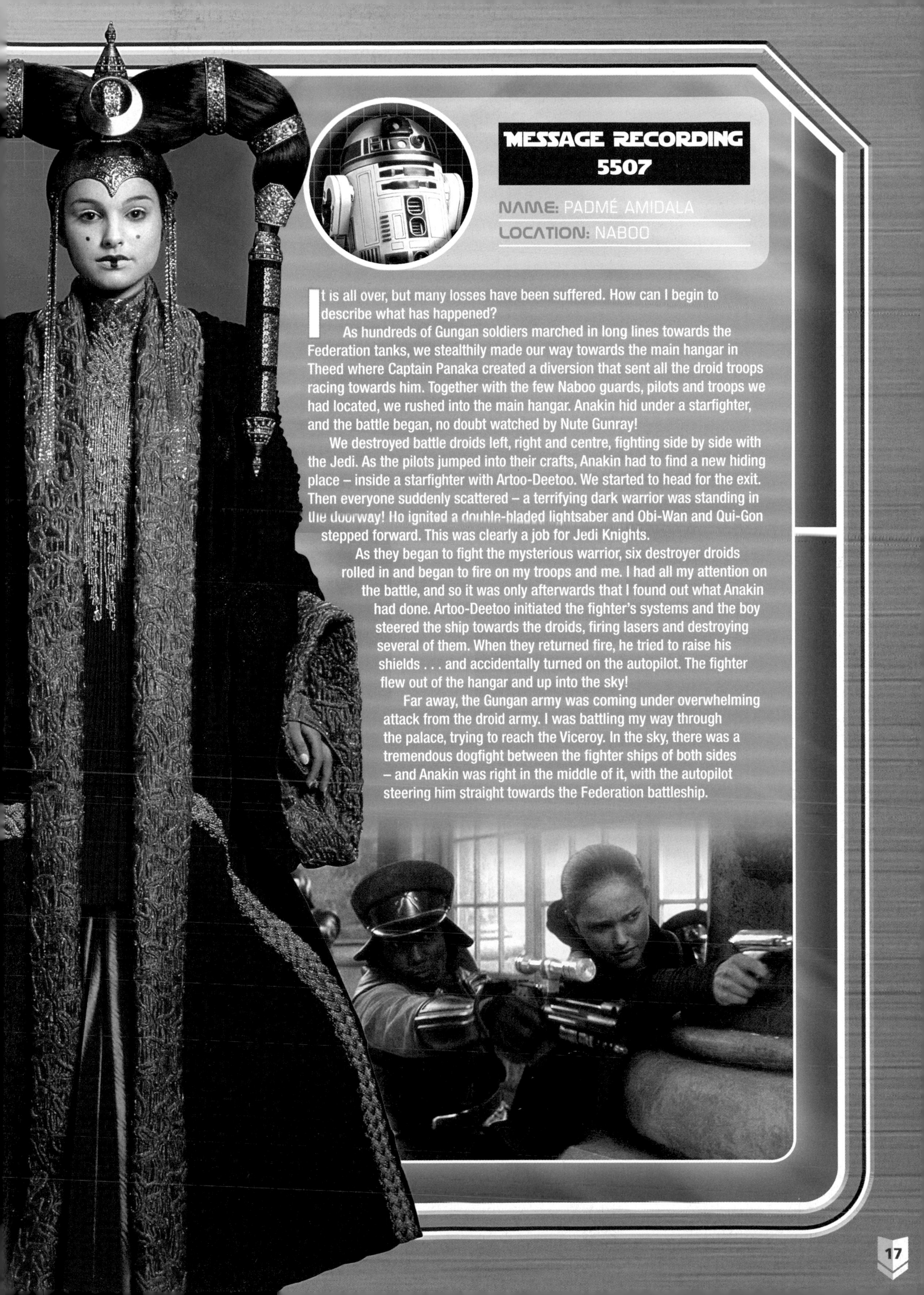

MESSAGE RECORDING 5507

NAME: PADMÉ AMIDALA

LOCATION: NABOO

It is all over, but many losses have been suffered. How can I begin to describe what has happened?

As hundreds of Gungan soldiers marched in long lines towards the Federation tanks, we stealthily made our way towards the main hangar in Theed where Captain Panaka created a diversion that sent all the droid troops racing towards him. Together with the few Naboo guards, pilots and troops we had located, we rushed into the main hangar. Anakin hid under a starfighter, and the battle began, no doubt watched by Nute Gunray!

We destroyed battle droids left, right and centre, fighting side by side with the Jedi. As the pilots jumped into their crafts, Anakin had to find a new hiding place – inside a starfighter with Artoo-Deetoo. We started to head for the exit. Then everyone suddenly scattered – a terrifying dark warrior was standing in the doorway! He ignited a double-bladed lightsaber and Obi-Wan and Qui-Gon stepped forward. This was clearly a job for Jedi Knights.

As they began to fight the mysterious warrior, six destroyer droids rolled in and began to fire on my troops and me. I had all my attention on the battle, and so it was only afterwards that I found out what Anakin had done. Artoo-Deetoo initiated the fighter's systems and the boy steered the ship towards the droids, firing lasers and destroying several of them. When they returned fire, he tried to raise his shields . . . and accidentally turned on the autopilot. The fighter flew out of the hangar and up into the sky!

Far away, the Gungan army was coming under overwhelming attack from the droid army. I was battling my way through the palace, trying to reach the Viceroy. In the sky, there was a tremendous dogfight between the fighter ships of both sides – and Anakin was right in the middle of it, with the autopilot steering him straight towards the Federation battleship.

MESSAGE RECORDING 5530

NAME: OBI-WAN KENOBI

LOCATION: CORUSCANT

While the Queen was confronting the Viceroy's defences, we were still battling the dark warrior. His moves were incredible. He fought both of us at once, flipping into the air and outmanoeuvring us at every turn. We fought our way across the narrow bridge of the Theed power generator. Then, in one terrible moment, the Sith Lord kicked me off one of the ramps and I fell several levels, leaving my Master to fight alone.

Above the planet, Anakin had regained control of the fighter and tried to join the battle, but he was hit and his ship spun into the hangar of the droid control ship.

I ran to catch up with the warriors. They had entered a long hallway filled with a series of laser doors, which opened and closed in a pattern every minute. The dark warrior was separated from my Master by one of the doors, but I was just starting into the hallway and was five doors away. I paced impatiently, my heart hammering as I waited for the doors to open. My Master sat and calmly meditated.

In the palace, the Queen had succeeded in capturing the Viceroy, but the Gungans were still losing their battle and the fighters in the sky were being destroyed.

As the fighting across the planet and in the skies above it intensified, the doors opened and I rushed towards my Master. The door between them now open, he was fighting the dark warrior again, moving into the small area around the power generator at the end of the hallway. The doors began to close again and I tried to reach my Master, but was caught behind yet another

door. I had to watch in frustration as the battle raged ferociously. Then, in the blink of an eye, my Master was caught off guard. It was all his attacker needed. The Sith Lord ran him through and Master Qui-Gon slumped to the floor in a heap.

I could not help myself – I screamed in rage and grief as the door opened and flung myself at the warrior. I was weary and my attacker was relentless. I slipped into the pit leading down to the generator's core and grabbed hold of a nozzle to stop myself falling, while my lightsaber fell down the shaft. The Sith Lord gave me a sickening grin as he prepared to kill me.

I called on all the wise training Master Qui-Gon had given me – all the wisdom of the Jedi Order and the strength of the Force. I jumped out of the pit, called my Master's lightsaber to me and cut the Sith Lord down. He fell into the core to his death.

There was no time to waste – I rushed to my Master's side. At once I knew that it was too late – I could sense that he was dying and I wept. His last words were about Anakin. I will record them here now. He said, "Promise me you'll train the boy. He is the Chosen One. He will bring balance. Train him!"

By some miracle, Anakin had survived. As I cradled Master Qui-Gon in my arms, the boy sent two torpedoes into the reactor room of the droid control ship. He escaped as the ship exploded, destroying all communication within the droid army. On the planet's surface, the droids shut down and froze.

We have won, but it has cost us dearly.

Senator Palpatine has been voted Supreme Chancellor. I hope that he will bring peace and prosperity to the Republic. The Naboo and the Gungans are celebrating their victory and new alliance, and Nute Gunray and his confederates are under arrest.

I have been granted the title of Jedi Knight, but I had some difficulty persuading the Council to allow me to take Anakin on as my Padawan. Yoda senses grave danger in his training, but I am sure that I can succeed. I have promised the boy that he will become a Jedi.

The Jedi Council is convinced that the warrior I fought was a Sith Lord. However, at any one time there are always two Sith Lords – a Master and an apprentice. Which one did I destroy?

The History of the Galactic Republic

The Galactic Republic was a democratic union of star systems, usually referred to as 'the Republic'. It was established a thousand years before the Battle of Naboo, following a conflict known as the Unification Wars. It grew as a result of increasingly sophisticated new means of communication and transportation, especially the development of hyperspace travel.

Over the millennia, the Republic came to encompass millions of inhabited worlds. It was originally a benevolent coalition, seeking peace throughout the galaxy and an end to such barbaric traditions as slavery. All member worlds of the Republic sent elected politicians to the Senate to create laws, pacts and treaties, and to govern the galactic union.

The Jedi Knights were the Republic's protectors and defenders. Arts and science blossomed, and for billions of sentient creatures, the time of the Republic was truly a golden age.

However, life under the Republic was not perfect. There were several almighty wars and they affected the entire galaxy. Over time, the Republic grew too large and became mired in corruption.

Greed and internal strife helped to destroy the Republic from within. Special interest groups and power-hungry individuals weakened the government and gave rise to apathy, social injustice, ineffectiveness and chaos.

Through stealth, cunning and betrayal, Senator Palpatine amassed great power within the Senate. He took control slowly, with amendment after amendment to the Constitution and executive directives. His ultimate aim was achieved when he issued Order 66 and replaced the Republic with the Empire.

GALACTIC REPUBLIC GOVERNMENT

22 BBY

SUPREME CHANCELLOR
Palpatine

CHANCELLOR'S OFFICE
Vice Chancellor
Aide: Sly Moore
Aide: Dar Wac
Personal Guard

MILITARY ADVISORY COUNCIL
Armand Isard
Mas Amedda
Senator Ha'Nouk
Sate Pestage

JEDI ORDER

JEDI HIGH COUNCIL

MASTERS
(Generals)

KNIGHTS
(Generals)

PADAWANS
(Commanders)

INITIATES
(Non-Combatants)

GRAND ARMY OF THE REPUBLIC

CLONE ARMY

SPECIAL OPERATIONS:
Commandos
ARC Troopers

LOYALIST COMMITTEE
1. Bail Antilles
2. Amidala
3. Orn Free Taa
4. Ask Aak
5. Ister Paddie
6. Lexie Dio
7. Onaconda Farr
8. Zo Holwer
9. Ronet Coorr
10. Darsana

SENATE

SUPREME COURT

JUDICIALS

GENERAL MINISTRY

Local planetary security forces of member worlds

ALLIES OF THE JEDI
Freedom's Sons
Antarian Rangers
Pendarran Warriors

SENATE GUARD

GALACTIC REPRESENTATIVE COMMISSION

SENATE BUREAU OF INTELLIGENCE

SENATE INVESTIGATION COMMITTEE

SECURITY AND INTELIGENCE COUNCIL

REPUBLIC SECURITY FORCE

SPACE RESCUE CORPS

REPUBLIC CORRECTIONAL AUTHORITY

Ministry of State
Ministry of Finance
Ministry of Commerce
Ministry of Security
Ministry of Science

OTHER:
Apprentice Legislature
Legislative Youth Programme
Refugee Relief Movement
Wildlife Commission

AGENCIES:
Navigation
Communications
Port Operations
Records
Facilities
Transportation

INSTITUTES:
Antiquities
Archaelology
Astrographic Survey
Engineering & Design
Galactic History
Sentient Studies

QUIZ

Part One

HOW WELL HAVE YOU STUDIED THE RECORDS AND DATA THAT HAVE TAUGHT US ABOUT THE HISTORY OF THE GALACTIC REPUBLIC? ANSWER THESE QUESTIONS TO FIND OUT IF YOU ARE AS KNOWLEDGEABLE AS YOU THINK!

QUESTION 1

Who was the Viceroy of the Trade Federation?

Nute Gunray

QUESTION 2

Why was Jar Jar Binks banished from Otoh Gunga?

He crashed Boss Nass's hey blibber

QUESTION 3

What was Padmé's real surname?

Naberrie

QUESTION 4

Who owned Shmi Skywalker?

Watto

QUESTION 5

Who was C-3PO's maker?

Anakin Skywalker

QUESTION 6

Who was the Senator for Naboo at the time of the blockade of Naboo?

Senator palpatine
~~Queen Amidala~~

QUESTION 7

What was the name of the captain of Queen Amidala's ship?

Captine panaka
~~Senator palpatine~~

QUESTION 8

Who proposed a vote of no confidence in Chancellor Valorum's leadership?

Queen Amidala

QUESTION 9

What was the name of Darth Sidious's first known apprentice?

Darth Maul

QUESTION 10

What species was Jar Jar Binks?

Gungan

Check your answers and give yourself a point for every correct answer. Keep a note of your scores.

PART 1 SCORE

10 out of **10**

MESSAGE RECORDING 7583

NAME: ANAKIN SKYWALKER

LOCATION: CORUSCANT

In all my life, I don't think I have ever felt as excited as I did yesterday, when I knew that I was going to see Padmé again. Even Master Obi-Wan noticed it. All my years of Jedi training could not help me to keep calm. After ten long years I was going to see Padmé again. I admit it, I was sweating!

The first person we saw was Jar Jar Binks, and he was so over-excited to see us that he helped me to calm down! Then I saw Padmé, and for me it was as if there was no one else in the room. Padmé greeted Master Obi-Wan and then looked at me. I found it hard to breathe. She is even more beautiful than I remember. Of course, I stammered and made a complete fool of myself. She laughed at me and shook her head, saying that I will always be the little boy she knew on Tatooine. I was so embarrassed – why can't she see how I've changed? I've thought about her every day since we parted . . . and she's forgotten me completely.

I must stop this! As Master Obi-Wan says I have to be mindful of my thoughts and stop focusing on the negative. I must think about our mission. Padmé is here for political reasons. That rat, Count Dooku, (sorry, Master Obi-Wan, I shouldn't lose my temper!) who abandoned the Jedi Order is now leading the

Separatist movement, encouraging planets to leave the Republic. Padmé came to the Galactic Senate to vote against creating an Army of the Republic. But as soon as she set foot on Coruscant there was an assassination attempt and her decoy was murdered. Of course I am not glad that such a terrible thing happened, but as a result she has been placed under the protection of Master Obi-Wan Kenobi and me. I can't help feeling pleased at the thought of spending time with her again!

MESSAGE RECORDING 7584

NAME: ANAKIN SKYWALKER

LOCATION: CORUSCANT

Last night was full of drama. Padmé had gone to bed but my Master and I were talking about Padmé and politics. I was tired – I haven't slept well since I started having these strange dreams about Mother. Master Obi-Wan yet again told me to be mindful of my thoughts. Then we both sensed the danger and raced into Padmé's bedroom. Two kouhuns were beside Padmé's bed, about to sting her! I destroyed the creatures with my lightsaber. My Master saw a probe droid outside the window and crashed straight through the window to grab it – a hundred storeys up! The probe droid sank under his weight but managed to say afloat, with my Master hanging on for dear life.

I was soon zooming after my Master in a speeder – just in time! The owner of the probe droid, a bounty hunter, shot at him and he fell fifty storeys before he landed in the passenger seat beside me. We had an exciting chase through the skies of Coruscant (with Master Obi-Wan complaining about my dangerous flying all the way – as if he doesn't know how good I am at it!). After almost losing the bounty hunter, we finally tracked her down in a nightclub. However, before she could tell us the name of the person who hired her, a toxic dart killed her. We saw an armoured rocket man taking off from a roof high above – we had no chance of catching him.

The Jedi Council has decided that Padmé must go back to Naboo for her own safety. The dead bounty hunter said enough to make us realise there will be more attempts on her life. It is my job to escort her and protect her. We will be travelling as refugees in unregistered transport. Obi-Wan does not think I am ready for this assignment, but he never appreciates my skills!

MESSAGE RECORDING 7599

NAME: OBI-WAN KENOBI

LOCATION: CORUSCANT

Everything is over, but I feel that it is important to make a record of the things that happened. The events of the past few days have led the whole galaxy towards a very dark time.

After my young apprentice left Coruscant to escort Senator Amidala home to Naboo, my job was to find out who had tried to assassinate her. Through an old friend I discovered that the toxic dart that had killed the bounty hunter was made on a planet called Kamino. However, when I searched for information about Kamino in the archive library, there was nothing to be found. The Archivist, Jocasta Nu, got rather annoyed when I suggested that the archives might be incomplete, insisting that if an item doesn't appear in the Jedi records, it doesn't exist.

It was Master Yoda who helped me to realise that someone has erased all record of Kamino from the archives. I travelled to the coordinates I had been given and sure enough, the planet Kamino was there. It is a watery world and the ultra-modern city of Tipoca stands on great stilts that keep it above the pounding waves.

I was astonished to find that I was expected on Kamino. At least, someone from the Jedi Order was expected. I discovered that the Kaminoans had been building a mighty clone army for the Republic, believing that they were under the orders of Master Sifo-Dyas almost ten years ago. But Master Sifo-Dyas died before that, and he never gave such instructions. I did not betray my surprise, but followed the Prime Minister, Lama Su, as he took me on a tour of the army.

I was amazed. Two hundred thousand units have been created. Another million are on the way. The clones are totally obedient, taking orders without question. The original host was a bounty hunter called Jango Fett. As soon as I heard this, I suspected that Jango Fett was the assassin I had been looking for. I asked to meet him, and when I caught a glimpse of his body armour my suspicions were confirmed.

I reported to the Jedi Council, who instructed me to take Jango into custody. However, he must have realised that he was in danger of being found out. I caught up with him as he was about to escape with his clone 'son' Boba. We fought, but he escaped and I was only just able to attach a small tracking device to his ship. I followed at a distance, but eventually he discovered the tracker and soon we were engaged in another battle, our ships flipping, rolling and turning at incredible speed. There were far too many near misses for my comfort – situations like those are exactly why I hate flying. I eventually tricked him into thinking that he had destroyed my ship, and then continued tracked him to the droid foundries on the planet of Geonosis by following his last known trajectory.

On Geonosis I came across Count Dooku and Nute Gunray of the Trade Federation, as well as the Archduke of Geonosis, Poggle the Lesser. I discovered that the Trade Federation was there to take delivery of a droid army. It was clear that Viceroy Gunray was behind the assassination attempts on Senator Amidala. The Commerce Guilds and Corporate Alliance had both pledged their armies to Count Dooku and were forming an alliance. I knew that I had to get this information to the Jedi Council as quickly as possible. My long-range transmitter had been knocked out, but I knew (or rather, I thought!) that Anakin was on Naboo. I tried to contact him there but with no luck. I widened the search and found his signal coming from Tatooine. There was no time to wonder that the blazes he was doing there. I asked him to transmit my message to the Council and started to speak, but as I started to talk, I was attacked!

MESSAGE RECORDING 7586

NAME: PADMÉ AMIDALA

LOCATION: NABOO

As we travelled in disguise to Naboo, I learned a lot more about Anakin. He told me about being a Jedi and how he feels that Obi-Wan is holding him back. I started to see that he is no longer the child I knew on Tatooine. He has changed a great deal. He also told me that recently he had been seeing his mother in his dreams, and that he was worried about her. Poor Anakin – his life has not been easy.

At last we arrived on Naboo. Anakin was delighted – he told me that when he had started his training, he had been very homesick and lonely. Thinking about his mother had made him feel worse, but thinking about Naboo had made him feel better.

We talked of politics and our childhoods. I tried to make Anakin understand how passionately I believe in democracy and reform. We visited the Queen and my family, and I think that for the first time Anakin saw me as a real person, not the angel he imagined I was when he was a child! My sister couldn't stop teasing me about him – she kept saying that it was obvious he had feelings for me!

Anakin and I travelled to the Naboo Lake Country – the perfect hiding place. Since I was a child, I cannot remember a time when I could relax so completely. And Anakin has been the best of companions. So direct and honest – so passionate. My feelings for him have grown day by day, but I know that I have to fight them. Anakin should be fighting them too, but he does not seem capable of it. I have to be strong for both of us.

On the first day, as we overlooked the water, Anakin kissed me. For a moment I was weak and I let him do it – but then I came to my senses and pulled away. It made me feel weak inside, and as a Senator, my role requires strength and focus.

The days passed by so beautifully in Anakin's company. He made me less serious – like I was as a child. Every moment drew me closer to him – and at the same time I could not give in to my feelings.

One evening at twilight, as we sat by the fire, Anakin declared his love for me openly – he laid his heart at my feet. In the world of politics, no one says how they truly feel. Anakin is so honest that it disarms me.

I had to make him see sense. I told him that we live in the real world, and Jedi aren't allowed to marry. I am determined not to give in to my feelings – there are more important things for me to do than to fall in love. At first he argued, but he could see that I was right. There can be no future for us.

Since then we have both tried to close off our feelings and forget them. I know that he finds it almost impossible. This morning, I joined him on the balcony overlooking the gardens. He was meditating, but he sensed my presence and asked me to stay. I knew that something was wrong – I can sense his every mood, and besides, I had heard him crying out in the night.

Anakin told me that he saw his mother in his nightmare. She was suffering and in pain. He is sure that it is real – that he is seeing true visions. He feels that he has to go to her – to save her. I cannot bear to see him in such pain, and I have agreed to go with him to Tatooine. That way he can continue to protect me and he won't be disobeying his orders.

MESSAGE RECORDING 7600

NAME: REPRESENTATIVE JAR JAR BINKS

LOCATION: CORUSCANT

Mesa berry proud un a lettal skeered. Many maxibig tings happenen since wesa comen Coruscant. Biggest ting is dat sum-un wishesan deaden M'lady Padmé! When wesa landen dersa biggen BOOM un poor Cordé, da decoy, was deaden. All berry shocken un da Jedi Council say needen two Jedi for protecten da Senator. Un big, big surprise, desa Jedi is Master Kenobi un lettal Annie! But nosa lettal bitty Annie now – hesa a biggen Padawan! Mesa no believen itsa him! But mesa so smilen to seein dem again.

M'lady Padmé is berry worryen abouten da vote un Anakin thinken shesa no happy to seein him. Hesa not knowen how serious desa politicky maken her. Shesa happier dan mesa seein her in longo time.

Den der unudder tryen to deaden da Senator! Wesa all skeered, but dose Jedi juss flyen after da baddie! Mesa sayen der no tings desa Jedi guys not do-en!

Da Jedi Council senden M'lady back to Naboo. Shesa no berry happy, but mesa representen Naboo in da Senate! Mesa berry honoured to be taken on dissa heavy burden. Mesa accept dis with muy muy humility.

Since M'lady Padmé shesa gone, things sliden from bad to badder. Master Obi-Wan in muy muy danger on Geonosis un da Commerce Guilds readyen maxibig war. Dersa many Jedi in da galaxy, but juss two hundred here now. Dat's no enough for war! Senator Ask Aak says wesa needen da clone army, but da Senate, deysa nebber approven usen da clones. Mesa tellen da Senators mesa proud to proposen da motion for granten emergency powers to da Chancellor. Mesa sure dis what M'lady Padmé would wanten mesa do.

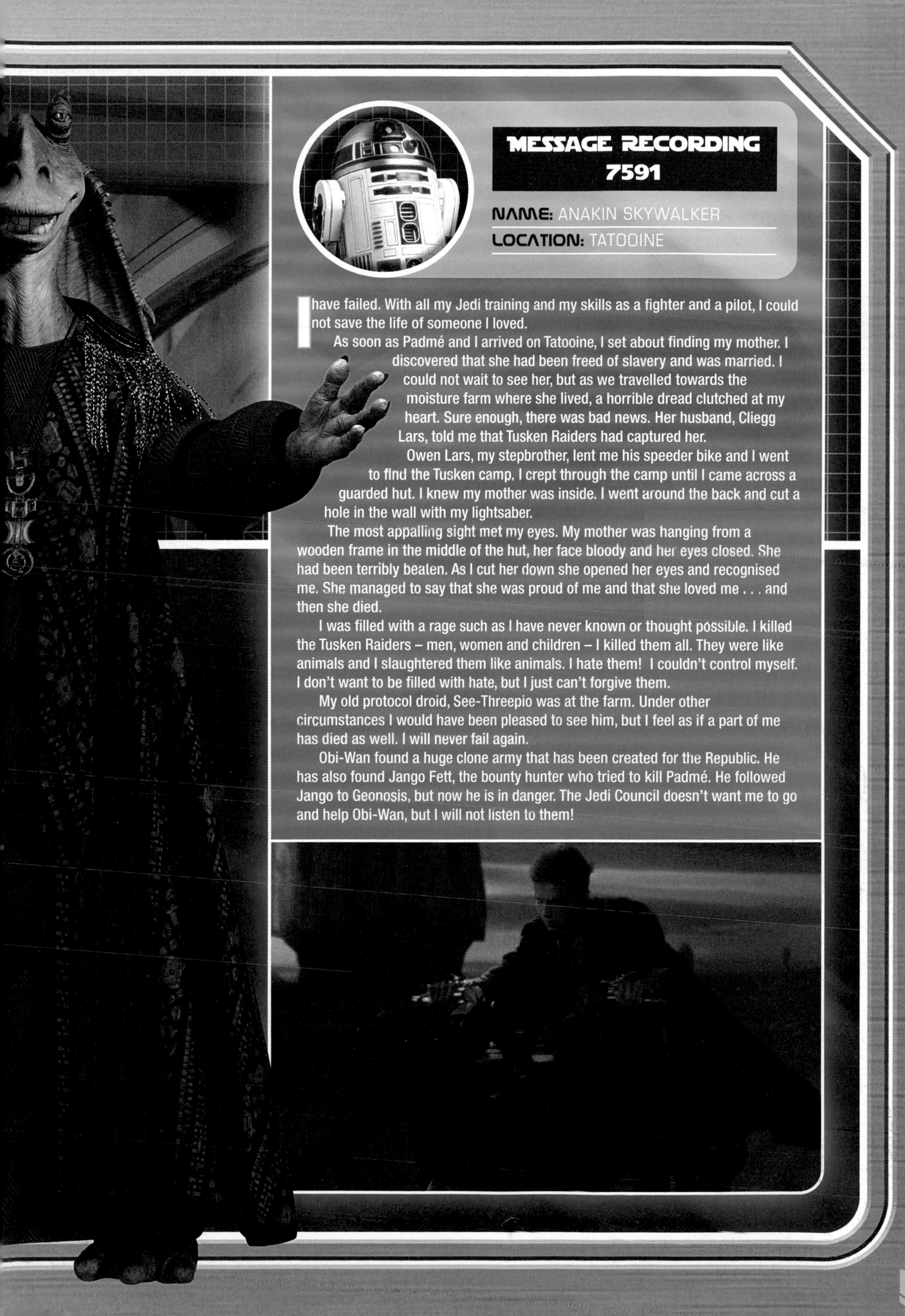

MESSAGE RECORDING 7591

NAME: ANAKIN SKYWALKER

LOCATION: TATOOINE

I have failed. With all my Jedi training and my skills as a fighter and a pilot, I could not save the life of someone I loved.

As soon as Padmé and I arrived on Tatooine, I set about finding my mother. I discovered that she had been freed of slavery and was married. I could not wait to see her, but as we travelled towards the moisture farm where she lived, a horrible dread clutched at my heart. Sure enough, there was bad news. Her husband, Cliegg Lars, told me that Tusken Raiders had captured her.

Owen Lars, my stepbrother, lent me his speeder bike and I went to find the Tusken camp. I crept through the camp until I came across a guarded hut. I knew my mother was inside. I went around the back and cut a hole in the wall with my lightsaber.

The most appalling sight met my eyes. My mother was hanging from a wooden frame in the middle of the hut, her face bloody and her eyes closed. She had been terribly beaten. As I cut her down she opened her eyes and recognised me. She managed to say that she was proud of me and that she loved me . . . and then she died.

I was filled with a rage such as I have never known or thought possible. I killed the Tusken Raiders – men, women and children – I killed them all. They were like animals and I slaughtered them like animals. I hate them! I couldn't control myself. I don't want to be filled with hate, but I just can't forgive them.

My old protocol droid, See-Threepio was at the farm. Under other circumstances I would have been pleased to see him, but I feel as if a part of me has died as well. I will never fail again.

Obi-Wan found a huge clone army that has been created for the Republic. He has also found Jango Fett, the bounty hunter who tried to kill Padmé. He followed Jango to Geonosis, but now he is in danger. The Jedi Council doesn't want me to go and help Obi-Wan, but I will not listen to them!

MESSAGE RECORDING 7593

NAME: C-3PO

LOCATION: GEONOSIS

Oh my circuits, the last few days have put me into such a spin! I don't think there's been a time in my life when I haven't been confused, but recent events are enough to make any self-respecting protocol droid go completely over the edge!

We arrived on Geonosis and Master Anakin landed the ship. Artoo-Deetoo wanted to go with Master Anakin and Mistress Padmé, but I told him quite clearly that if they had needed our help, they would have asked for it. I do wish that annoying little unit would listen to me. Of course, he didn't pay any attention to me, but raced off down the landing ramp at top speed. I followed him as fast as I could – he has no sense whatsoever, and he might need help.

We reached a small walkway and saw a monstrous droid factory, full of stamping machines and welders. It was very strange – machines creating machines! Master Anakin and Mistress Padmé were battling terrifying creatures, and then that wretched little unit pushed me off the walkway! I landed on a conveyer belt as Artoo flew off to help Mistress Padmé.

Then began a very unpleasant time for me. I knew my maker was in danger, but there was nothing I could do about it! My head was sliced from my body and welded to a battle droid body. As I was carried away on another conveyer belt, I saw that Mistress Padmé and Master Anakin had been captured. I was sure that we were doomed.

Anakin and I were taken to Count Dooku, who tried to persuade me to join the Separatists. Of course I refused, so he turned me over to the Geonosians. In a laughable pretence of a trial, Anakin and I were sentenced to death.

The Geonosians threw us into a cart and took us to the execution arena. We could hear a vast crowd, baying for our blood. I had to tell Anakin how I really felt about him. If we were going to die, there was no reason to hold back. I told him that I love him. I told him that my love for him is a puzzle for which I have no answers. I can't control it.

I kissed him, and the next moment we were taken into the blinding sunlight of the arena. We saw that Master Obi-Wan was chained to one of four upright posts. Anakin and I were chained to two more.

I had a wire hidden in my clothing, and I pulled it out and put it in my mouth. My arms were pulled high above my head, and I knew the same thing was happening to Anakin and Master Obi-Wan. Then, from different gates around the arena, four monsters were driven in – a reek, an orray, a nexu and an acklay. I used the wire to pick the lock on one of the hand restraints, and then I pulled myself up by the chain to the top of the post. I knew that Anakin and Master Obi-Wan would fight as hard as me – either we would escape or we would make our deaths cost them dear!

We were beating the dreadful Geonosian monsters, but then droidekas rolled into the arena and surrounded us. I thought that our end had come, but then, in the archducal box, I saw a sight that changed everything for the better. Master Mace Windu was there!

MESSAGE RECORDING
7594

NAME: PADMÉ AMIDALA

LOCATION: GEONOSIS

MESSAGE RECORDING 7601

NAME: MACE WINDU

LOCATION: GEONOSIS

We got into position just in time – Master Obi-Wan, Senator Amidala and Anakin had put up a good fight against the beasts, but the droidekas were a different story. I had crept into the archducal box, ignited my lightsaber and held it to Jango Fett's neck. Count Dooku masked his surprise elegantly. He was not even alarmed when, all around the arena, a hundred Jedi switched on their lightsabers.

As thousands of battle droids poured into the arena, Jango Fett fired his flamethrower at me and the battle began. Geonosians flew away in all directions. Droids fired at Jedi, who cut them down as the beasts stampeded. I fought back to back with Master Obi-Wan, while Senator Amidala and Anakin did the same. We swiped and mangled droids, but the Jedi were slowly being driven back. We killed heaps of Geonosians and destroyed piles of droids, but their numbers got the better of us. Slowly but surely, we were all driven into the centre of the arena. I fought a particularly fierce duel with Jango Fett, who was a powerful warrior. However, eventually I cut off his head and his body fell to the ground. Out of the corner of my eye, I saw Artoo-Deetoo rescuing See-Threepio, whose head was attached to a battle droid's body.

At last it seemed as if the end had come. We stood in the centre of the arena surrounded by a ring of battle droids. The bloodied sand was strewn with bodies. Count Dooku offered to spare our lives if we surrendered, but we were not prepared to become hostages for him to barter with. He raised his hand to give the order to fire . . . and then Senator Amidala gave a cry. Six gunships descended towards us. Master Yoda had arrived with the clone troopers – just in time!

WITNESS RECORD

NAME: R2-D2

LOCATION: NABOO

In conjunction with protocol droid C-3PO, I, R2-D2, witnessed the marriage of Anakin Skywalker and Padmé Amidala. We have been programmed to keep this information a secret.

Terrified the Separatists our massive army did. As the clone troopers opened fire on the Geonosians and the massed droids, knew that Nute Gunray and Poggle the Lesser would be panicking I did. However, capture Count Dooku we had to. If he should escape, more systems to his cause would he rally. Trade Federation starships began to take off. I let the Force flow through me, directing the clone troopers.

From their gunship, Anakin and Master Obi-Wan saw Count Dooku making his escape towards the hangar tower, and chased after his speeder they did. Moments later, the clone commander reported that the droid army was in full retreat. I took my ship and followed Master Obi-Wan – I sensed that needed I would be.

When I arrived in the hangar tower, badly wounded Master Obi-Wan was and Anakin had lost his arm and was about to lose his life. Battled with Dooku did I, and tried everything from levitating machinery to attacking me with Force lightning he did. Powerful he had become –the dark side in him I could sense. A mighty lightsaber duel we fought and my old Padawan battled well, but defeat me he could not.

At last he realised that win he could not. He used the Force to pull on one of the cranes, sending it crashing down towards Anakin and Obi-Wan. Tried to hold the crane off by using the Force they did, but strong enough they weren't. Help them I did, but as I concentrated and moved the crane aside, escaped did Dooku.

Darth Sidious, the Sith Master, controls the Senate Dooku said. Become unreliable, Dooku has. Lies, deceit and mistrust are his ways now. Nevertheless, a closer eye on the Senate I feel we should keep. A hollow victory this is. As I watched tens of thousands of clone troops entering their assault Ships, sense that this was only the beginning I could. Begun, this clone war has!

MESSAGE RECORDING 7602

NAME: YODA

LOCATION: CORUSCANT

The History of the SITH

THE SITH EMPIRE

Although at one time the Sith Empire was a great and terrible power of evil in the galaxy, it fell over five thousand years before the Battle of Yavin. In the final stages of the Great Hyperspace War, the forces of the Old Republic (led by the Empress Teta) pursued the Sith warlords across the galaxy.

The Sith were driven to near extinction, but a small number found sanctuary on Yavin 4, under the command of Dark Lord Naga Sadow. Battered and broken, the Sith disappeared into the shadows of history and were all but forgotten.

THE SITH ORDER

About two millennia before the Galactic Civil War, a rogue Jedi Knight turned away from the Order and began a new Sith cult. He believed that the real power of the Force came from the dark side. Other members of the Order who shared his belief soon joined the fallen Jedi. More were recruited, and the Sith Order eventually grew to over fifty in number. They existed only to dominate and control.

THE SITH WARS

Initially, the Sith battled the Jedi with great ferocity. However, internal conflicts soon distracted the group. Greed and the pursuit of power led to feuding within the Sith Order. These struggles continued for centuries. The Sith made war on the Jedi while at the same time slaughtering one after another of their own leaders, such as Belia Darzu, the Dark Underlord, and Darth Rivan. As soon as one Dark Lord fell, another took up the title.

The hostilities finally erupted into a violent, galaxy-spanning conflict. The Sith Brotherhood of Darkness battled the Jedi Order's Army of Light as well as each other. They destroyed their leader first, and then wiped out one another. The few who escaped this bloodbath were destroyed by the Jedi. In a matter of weeks, it seemed that all the Sith had been slain and the Order extinct. However, one man remained – Darth Bane.

DARTH BANE

As part of the Sith Order, Bane had adopted cunning and stealth as his methods. While the other Sith destroyed one another, he stood aside and watched. After the destruction of the Sith Order, Darth Bane went into hiding to avoid the Jedi. Then, when the time was right, he sought out an apprentice.

Bane swore that he would have his revenge on the Jedi. He understood and accepted that his revenge could take hundreds of years, so he established two rules to guide and protect future generations of Sith Lords. First, the Sith would remain hidden until the perfect opportunity arose to avenge themselves. Second, there would only ever be two Sith Lords at any given time, a Master and an apprentice. This tradition dated back to the Sith Lords of the ancient past, and the Sith remained loyal to this code for almost a thousand years. The two Sith would work in tandem, establishing a balance of power. They would survive in secrecy, waiting until the Sith Master thought that the Jedi were vulnerable. At this moment, the Sith would strike.

Bane trained his apprentice, stressing that their enemy was the Jedi Order and not each other. Eventually, Bane's apprentice became a Sith Master and sought out her own apprentice, thus ensuring that the Sith legacy would survive.

The title of Dark Lord was passed down from one generation to the next, with only one or two Dark Lords existing at any given time. The mummified remains of many of the Dark Lords are preserved in monumental temples on Korriban.

THE REVENGE OF THE SITH

Over a thousand years after the death of the Darth Bane, Darth Sidious carried on the Sith legacy. He decided that the time had come to take over the Republic, but he knew he could have only one assistant. He plotted behind the scenes, set up situations that he could control and used other people to get things to happen according to his plans. His cunning and hatred would eventually lead to the near-extinction of the Jedi Order and a time of dark despair for the galaxy.

QUIZ

Part Two

ANSWER THESE QUESTIONS ABOUT THE START OF THE CLONE WARS AND ADD YOUR SCORE TO YOUR TOTAL FROM PART 1.

QUESTION 1

What was the name of Senator Amidala's decoy?

Cord'e ....

QUESTION 2

Who did Senator Amidala appoint as her representative in the Senate?

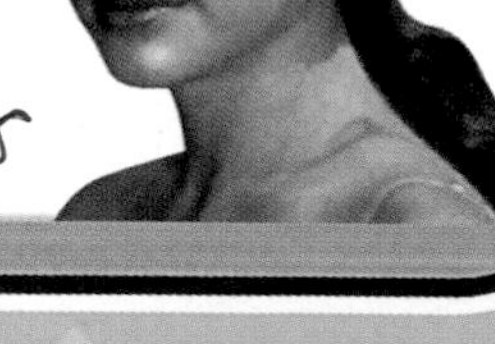

Jar Jar binks ....

QUESTION 3

Who told Obi-Wan where the toxic dart came from?

Dexter ....

QUESTION 4

Why did Anakin slaughter the Tusken Raiders?

Revenge – they killed his mother

QUESTION 5

What was the name of Padmé's sister?

Sola

QUESTION 6

Who did Anakin see in his dreams?

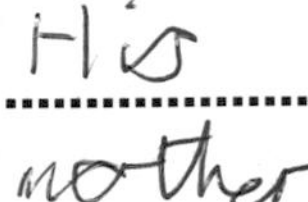

His mother

QUESTION 7

What were the names of the beasts in the Geonosian arena?

reek, orray, nexu, acklay

QUESTION 8

What was Count Dooku's Sith name?

Darth Tyranus

QUESTION 9

Who witnessed Senator Amidala's marriage?

C3PO and R2-D2

QUESTION 10

What were the Geonosians building for the Separatists?

A droid army

PART 2 SCORE

10 out of **10**

MESSAGE RECORDING 9863

NAME: ANAKIN SKYWALKER

LOCATION: CORUSCANT

It is three years since the Clone Wars began, but it feels like thirty. I have learned so much. Our massive army has fought many deadly battles with the Separatist droid army, the Galactic Republic is crumbling and the Jedi have suffered massive casualties . . . and still the fighting goes on. I know that some citizens are beginning to doubt whether the Jedi really have the galaxy's best interests in mind.

Supreme Chancellor Palpatine has been a guide and a mentor to me. When we found that the fiendish droid leader, General Grievous, had kidnapped him, Obi-Wan and I went on a desperate mission to rescue him.

After a dangerous battle, we entered General Grievous's starship in near space above the planet's surface. We found the Supreme Chancellor shackled to a chair in the main room of Grievous' quarters. Before I could untie him, Count Dooku strode into the room with two super battle droids. I was determined that Dooku would not get away with this. I had fought him once at the start of the Clone Wars and lost my lower arm. But the Clone Wars have made me into a far better warrior, and I knew that I could defeat him.

Dooku knocked Obi-Wan out and taunted me, saying that I should use my hate and anger. A new ferociousness seemed to enter me and in moments he was at my mercy. The Supreme Chancellor urged me to kill him. I knew that the Council would not want me to do it, but in that moment, I didn't care. I sliced Dooku's evil head from his body.

With laser fire still rocking the command ship, we tried to escape, engaging yet more super battle droids as well as Grievous and his bodyguards. Suddenly, alarms signalled that the cruiser was falling out of orbit. Grievous rushed to the escape pod bay and launched himself into space, and I managed to land the ship on Coruscant.

As soon as I was back on Coruscant, I sensed the presence of the one person I love above all others. I slipped away and found Padmé waiting for me. Putting my arms around my wife after five long months apart was one of the happiest moments of my life. I only wish we didn't have to keep our marriage secret. The next moment my emotions were turned upside down again, as she told me that she is pregnant! It is the best news in the world – I just wish she would stop being so worried about people finding out. We have kept our secret this long, after all!

My happiness was short-lived though. Last night, I had one of my most vivid nightmares. I saw my beautiful Padmé dying in childbirth, frightened and without me. I awoke in a horrifying panic. It was just like the dreams I used to have about my mother before she died. I am so scared of losing her. Padmé suggested that I tell Obi-Wan, but I can't do that. He has been a brother to me, but he's on the Council. I don't need his help. Instead, I have been to see Master Yoda. I didn't tell him that the dream was about Padmé – only that it was about someone close to me. Master Yoda just cautioned me to be careful when sensing the future. He said that the fear of loss is a path to the dark side, and that death is a natural part of life. But he doesn't know how much I love Padmé – he can't understand. I won't let these visions come true.

Obi-Wan met me to say that Chancellor Palpatine wanted to see me. He is suspicious of the Chancellor for some reason, and is full of dark warnings. I hurried to see my mentor. He said that he is proud of my achievements, and he trusts me. If only Obi-Wan could see me as the Chancellor does! The Chancellor has asked for my help. He fears the Jedi and feels that we are shrouded in secrecy. He has appointed me as his representative on the Jedi Council! I am to be the eyes, ears and voice of the Republic! It is a great honour – but I am not sure the Council will accept this appointment.

MESSAGE RECORDING 9872

NAME: PADMÉ AMIDALA

LOCATION: CORUSCANT

Earlier, in Bail Organa's office, a group of us came together to discuss the fact that the Chancellor now has control of the Jedi Council. Senators Mon Mothma, Fang Zar, Terr Taneel and Giddean Danu were there with Bail Orgna and me. We are all agreed that the Chancellor has become an enemy of democracy. He has emergency powers, control of the Jedi Council and governors overseeing all star systems in the Republic. The constitution is in shreds.

I can hardly believe it has come to this. Chancellor Palpatine is one of my oldest advisors – he served as my Ambassador when I was Queen. But corruption has taken hold in the Senate. Palpatine has become a dictator, and we have helped him do it. We have agreed that we will form an organisation of loyalists, trying to preserve democracy in the Republic. We have also agreed that we must not discuss this with anyone, even our families. It hurts me to hide things from Anakin, but I know that he trusts and respects the Chancellor. He would not understand.

Anakin is angry. He is on the Jedi Council, but they have not granted him the rank of Master. He feels that he is more powerful than any of them, and he had an outburst in front of them all, raging against their decision. My darling, why can't you see that they are worried by your lack of self-control?

The Council wants him to report on all of the Chancellor's dealings.

They want to know what he's up to. Anakin is upset that the Council want him to spy on his good friend and mentor, but for now he is being guided by Obi-Wan, and will honour the Council's request.

My baby has started kicking – it is wonderful to feel our child growing. But I am afraid, too – afraid of what I sometimes see in Anakin's eyes. I tried to talk to him about the Chancellor, suggesting that perhaps the Republic has become the very evil we are trying to destroy. Anakin grew angry, saying I sounded like a Separatist. I know the Chancellor listens to him. I asked him to persuade the Chancellor to stop the fighting and let diplomacy resume, but he took it badly. He told me to make a motion in the Senate, not to use him as an errand boy. He can sense that there are things I am not telling him, but he is shutting me out as well.

MESSAGE RECORDING 9873

NAME: ANAKIN SKYWALKER

LOCATION: CORUSCANT

The Chancellor has told me some disturbing things. He began by saying that his clone intelligence units have located General Grievous on the planet Utapau. However, he then told me that the Jedi Council is plotting to betray him. I had to admit that my trust in them has been shaken.

The Chancellor went on to say that the Jedi point of view is not the only true one, and that the Dark Lords of the Sith also believe in security and justice. He said that the Sith and the Jedi are similar in almost every way, including their quest for greater power. The difference between the two is that the Sith are not afraid of the dark side of the Force. That is why they are more powerful.

I feel so confused. The Jedi are selfless and use their power only to help others, while the Sith are selfish, using their powers only to help themselves. But the Chancellor says this isn't true. He told me about Darth Plagueis, a Sith Lord who was powerful and wise. He apparently had such a knowledge of the dark side that he could even keep the ones he cared about from dying.

When I heard that, it was as if a magnet was drawing me towards it. Above all, I must stop my dreams from coming true. This power – this ability – is part of the Force. I have to learn how to use it! I will become more powerful with this new knowledge of the Force, and I will save Padmé.

The Jedi Council has decided to send Obi-Wan to face Grievous, despite the fact that the Chancellor wants me to lead the campaign and despite the fact that Obi-Wan was not so successful the last time he met Grievous.

MESSAGE RECORDING 9889

NAME: OBI-WAN KENOBI

LOCATION: UTAPAU

Before leaving to find Grievous, I visited Padmé at her apartment. The time was right to talk to her about what I know. I have known for some time that the two of them are in love. I told her how worried I am about Anakin, because he has become so moody and detached. He has changed since returning to Coruscant. I promised her that I won't tell the Council about their relationship, but asked her to do what she can to help Anakin.

On my way to Utapau, I put my concerns about Anakin out of my mind and focused on my mission. When I arrived I was greeted by the local administrator, Tion Medon. I told him that I wanted some fuel for my ship and to use the city as a base as I searched nearby systems for General Grievous, but Tion Medon drew close to me, looking scared. The General was holding them hostage. Grievous and thousands of battle droids were stationed on the tenth level.

I instructed Tion Medon to tell his people to take shelter and his warriors to prepare for battle. I then returned to my starfighter and told my astromech droid, R4-G9, that I was staying on the planet. I wanted him to take off and tell Commander Cody that I had made contact.

I watched my fighter leave and then looked up at the tenth level. I had to figure out how I was going to get up there. Eventually I came across a corral filled with dragon-like lizards. Using the Force, I influenced a nearby wrangler to give me a lizard called Boga and I swung up on to her back. She reared up and then scurried off, climbing the wall of the sheer cliff.

I found Grievous standing before the Council of Separatists. Nute Gunray was there, along with Poggle the Lesser, Rune Haako and a host of other cowardly warmongers. Grievous was telling the Council that it would only be a matter of time before their enemies

knew where they were hiding and sent them to the Mustafar system in the Outer Rim.

After they left, I followed the General to the control centre and revealed my presence. The General commanded his bodyguards to attack me, but they were no match for a trained Jedi. I cut one down and then used the Force to bring the roof down on the rest.

Grievous told his guards to back away. The foul creature separated his four arms and each hand grabbed a lightsaber from his belt. He attacked me in a flashing display of swordsmanship, driving me all the way across the control centre. I mounted a counter-attack as battle droids begin firing on me. Suddenly, dozens of clone troopers charged into the control centre, guns blazing. My message had reached Commander Cody.

Grievous raced towards one of the landing platforms. He jumped on to a wheel bike and took off down the wall. I could not let him escape a second time! I jumped on to Boga's back and chased after Grievous, unfortunately dropping my lightsaber as I went.

After a long chase through the city, I finally caught up with Grievous. I leaped off Boga and on to the General's bike, knocking them both to the ground.

The brutal cyborg was deadly and unstoppable, but then I noticed that his stomach plate was loose. I ripped it off and saw the bag that contained Grievous' organic innards. He hoisted me over his head, tossing me across the platform. As I dangled off the edge, Grievous grabbed his electrostaff and charged at me. At the last second, I reached out with the Force to grab his blaster and fired it into Grievous's stomach. He exploded from the inside out.

It was one of the most uncivilised battles of my entire career.

MESSAGE RECORDING 9896

NAME: DARTH VADER

LOCATION: CORUSCANT

EVERYTHING HAS CHANGED.

When he heard that Grievous had been found, Chancellor Palpatine warned me that I had to be careful of the Jedi. He told me that they fear me, and in time they will destroy me. Then he revealed to me the full truth, asking me to allow him to train me.

He promised to teach me the subtleties of the Force – subtleties that could help me to break through the fog of lies the Council has created. He finally stated that he knows the nature of the dark side. What he can teach me can help me to save Padmé's life.

Fool that I was, I grew angry and confused. At that time I still believed that the Sith were my enemy. I ignited my lightsaber, while the Chancellor urged me to follow his lead. He tried to tell me that my anger would give me focus and make me stronger, but I wouldn't listen. The Jedi had brainwashed me well! I decided to turn him over to the Jedi Council.

I told Master Windu that the Chancellor knew the ways of the Force and had been trained to use the dark side. I wanted to go with Master Windu and the other Jedi to the Chancellor's office, but he refused. He told me that fear was clouding my judgement – and I listened to him. He and three other Jedi went off to arrest the Chancellor.

As soon as they had gone, their influence left me and I started to think more clearly. I realised that if they killed the Chancellor, I would lose my only chance of saving Padmé's life. Nothing matters more to me than that. I sped to the Chancellor's office, hoping that I would be in time.

I arrived just in time to see Master Windu knock the Chancellors' lightsaber out of his hand.

He declared that the oppression of the Sith would never return. The Chancellor became enraged, shooting bolts of lightning out of his hands at Master Windu, which the Jedi blocked with his lightsaber. I had never seen anything like it! Windu pushed the Chancellor right to the edge of the ledge, and as he moved closer, the bolts of

lightning began to arch back towards the Sith Lord. The Chancellor's face started to twist and distort, and his eyes became yellow as he struggled to intensify his powers. He begged for his life, but Master Windu seemed determined not to let him get away.

I could not believe what I was seeing. According to all I had been taught, the Chancellor had to stand trial. I cried out in protest, but Mace would not listen. He said that the Chancellor was too dangerous to be left alive.

I thought of Padmé and all the Jedi nonsense left my head. I lunged forward and cut off Master Windu's lightsaber arm. As he stared at me in shock, the Chancellor sprang to life, bombarding Master Windu with powerful bolts of lightning. Unable to deflect the blasts with just one hand, he was flung out of the window and fell to his death.

The Chancellor laughed, and for a moment I was horrified by his deformed face and his cackling delight. But he encouraged me to fulfil my destiny and become his apprentice – to learn to use the dark side of the Force. In some ways it was the most terrible choice of my life, but it came down to the difference between life and death for Padmé. I can't live without her. I need the power to stop death.

I knelt before my Master and pledged myself to his teachings and the ways of the Sith. From that moment on, I would be known as Darth Vader.

Every single Jedi, including Obi-Wan, is now an enemy of the Republic. I must go to the Temple to destroy all the Jedi there, and then to the Mustafar system to wipe out Nute Gunray and the other Separatist leaders. At last, Palpatine and I will rule.

MESSAGE RECORDING 9914

NAME: OBI-WAN KENOBI

LOCATION: POLIS MASSA

My satisfaction at ending Grievous's miserable life did not last long. To my utter amazement, the clone troopers turned on me. I now know that Palpatine had transformed fully into Darth Sidious, and had instructed the clone commanders to carry out Order 66: Destroy all Jedi.

I escaped the attack, but across the galaxy many of my fellow Jedi were not so lucky. As soon as I could, I returned to Grievous' secret landing platform, boarded a starfighter and headed away from Utapau. I made contact with Bail Organa, who said that he had rescued Master Yoda. I headed for the *Tantive IV*, Bail Organa's cruiser.

None of us knew what had happened or if any of the other Jedi were alive. Yoda explained that he had received a coded message that told all the Jedi to return to the Temple because the war is over. I knew that we had to dismantle the coded signal. If there were other survivors like us, they would fall into the trap and be killed.

Master Yoda and I entered the Temple to dismantle the coded signal. The bodies of young students lay everywhere. Not even the younglings had survived.

We recalibrated the code and then went to find out who had done this terrible thing. In the hologram area, we discovered the images of the slaughter.

What I saw broke my heart. The image showed Anakin slaughtering Jedi, both young and old. We watched Anakin kneel before the dark-robed figure of Lord Sidious – whom we now know is Palpatine.

We had to destroy the Sith, and I begged Master Yoda to send me to kill Palpatine. How could I fight and destroy the boy I trained? But Master Yoda said that I am not strong enough to fight Lord Sidious. He would face Sidious, and I would have to kill my former Padawan.

I went to Padmé's apartment, where we shared our news: The Republic had fallen and the Jedi Order was no more. Padmé had hope because the Senate was still intact, but I knew that the Sith now ruled the galaxy. I told her that Anakin had turned to the dark side – that he killed all the younglings, but she refused to believe me. I guessed that Anakin was the father of her child, and was desperately sorry for her. But I had to stop Anakin before he hurt anyone else.

I was certain that Padmé knew where Anakin had gone, and sure enough she soon prepared her skiff to leave Coruscant. I secretly boarded the

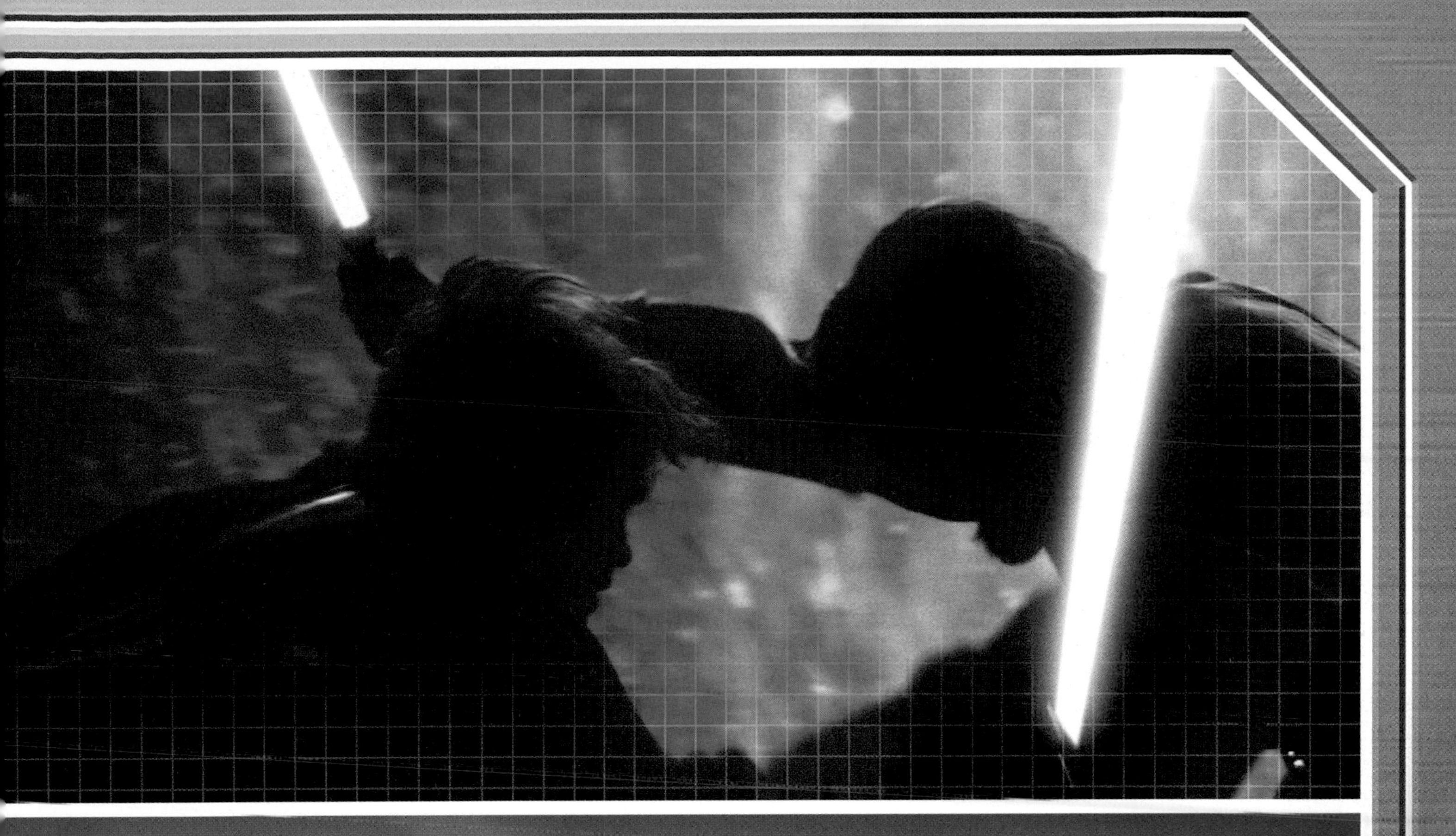

ship. She unknowingly took me to Anakin.

The skiff landed on Mustafar and I saw Anakin rush to greet Padmé. She questioned him about what I had said, but he grew enraged at the mention of my name. Too late, she realised how much he had changed. I moved to the doorway of the skiff and Anakin saw me. He thought Padmé had betrayed him.

To my horror he grabbed Padmé by the throat and began choking her. I begged him to let her go, and at last he released his grip. Padmé crumpled to the ground. He accused me of turning her against me, but he had done that himself. Anakin became the very thing he had sworn to destroy.

We began our battle. It ranged across the main control centre and out on to the balcony, which collapsed, tumbling us towards the lava river. We jumped from one multi-spire panel to another, risking our lives, until I jumped towards the safety of the black sandy edge of the river, gaining the high ground. I was grieving for the boy I had trained, knowing that I had failed him. Anakin sneered at me and tried to follow me, but I cut him at the knees, and cut off his left arm in the blink of an eye. He fell down the embankment, rolling to a stop near the edge of the lava. I picked up his lightsaber and looked back.

"I hate you!" Anakin cried. The sound will never stop ringing in my ears. Anakin was my brother and I loved him. His clothing dipped into the lava and ignited. He was engulfed in flames and started screaming, struggling to crawl back up the embankment. I turned and went back to Padmé's ship.

On Coruscant, Master Yoda had failed to destroy Darth Sidious. Bail Organa rescued him, but we must all go into exile now.

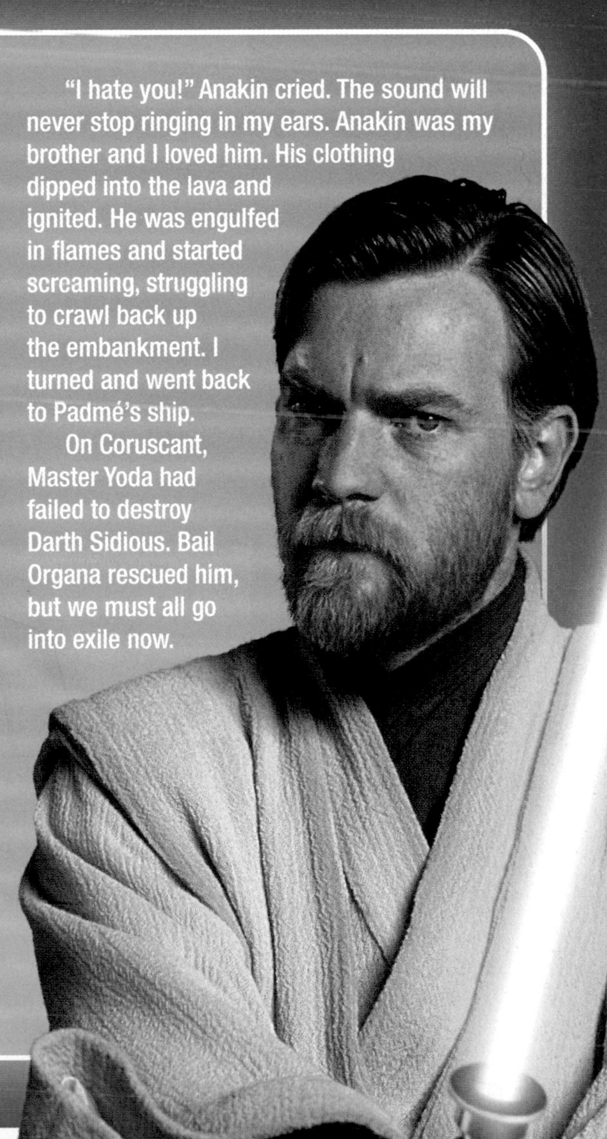

MESSAGE RECORDING 9915

NAME: C-3PO

LOCATION: POLIS MASSA

Oh my maker, we are surrounded by tragedy. Poor, poor Mistress Padmé. As soon as Master Kenobi and Master Anakin began to fight, I carried her into the skiff. Master Anakin had choked her and she was unconscious. Artoo-Detoo was in a terrible panic. I lay her on a bed inside the ship and waited anxiously. After what seemed like an eternity, Master Kenobi appeared. He looked as though he had aged ten years, but he hurried inside the skiff and we took off. Mistress Padmé woke up briefly, but only to ask if Master Anakin was all right. Master Kenobi could not answer her.

We landed on the isolated asteroid of Polis Massa, where we were met by Master Yoda and Bail Organa. Mistress Padmé was quickly taken to the asteroid's medical centre, where the Polis Massa medics worked on her in the operating room.

A medical droid explained that medically, she was completely healthy. She just seemed to have lost the will to live, and it seems that this can kill a human. The droid then revealed that she was carrying twins! Master Yoda grew concerned at this and said that these babies were the last hope.

Artoo and I waited while the medical droids rushed to and fro. I had to explain about the reproductive process to Artoo. He really is a rather ignorant little astromech droid sometimes. Master Kenobi was with Padmé as she gave birth, first to a boy called Luke and then to a girl called Leia.

Although the babies were safe, Mistress Padmé could not seem to find the will to live. She died speaking of Master Anakin, trying to persuade Master Kenobi that there is still good in him.

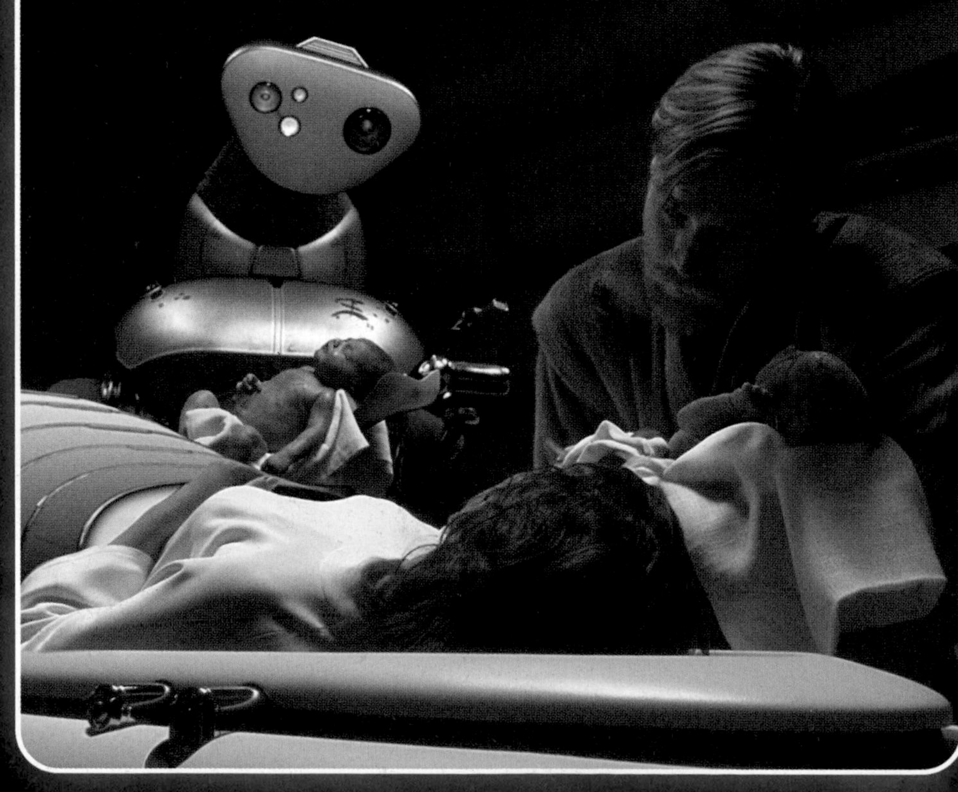

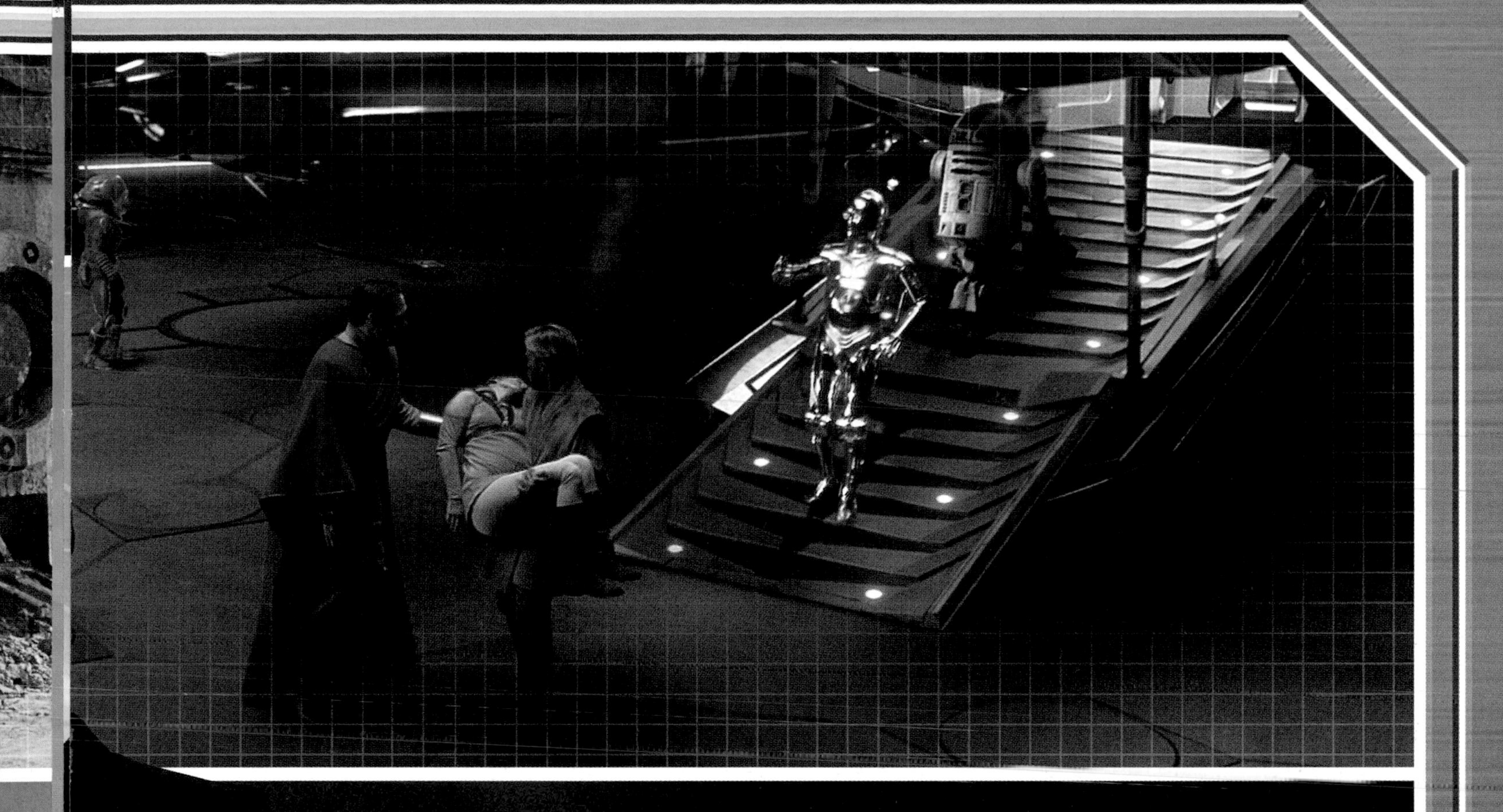

MESSAGE RECORDING 9916

NAME: BAIL ORGANA

LOCATION: ALDERAAN

Aboard my cruiser, Yoda, Obi-Wan and I made the necessary plans to send Padmé's body back to Naboo. She still needs to appear pregnant, because the children must be hidden and kept somewhere safe where the Sith will never sense their presence. Eventually we agreed that it was best for the children to be split up.

My wife and I will take the girl. She will be loved with us, and we have longed for a family. I know that my wife will agree. Obi-Wan will take the boy to Tatooine, where his family lives. There he will stay in hiding, so that he can watch over the child as he grows.

Will Anakin's children be able to defeat Lord Sidious? It is hard to believe now – everything seems so dark. But as Master Yoda says, the Force runs strong in the Skywalker line. We can only hope.

I left the conference room and took Artoo Deetoo and See-Threepio to Captain Antilles. They needed to be cleaned up, and I decided that Threepio's mind should be wiped. Artoo is a sturdy little astromech droid who understands the significance of these events, but a protocol droid cannot be expected to keep secrets.

And so, across the galaxy, the preparations begin. On the planet of Naboo, a large crowd has gathered to pay their final respects to Padmé as she is laid to rest. Master Yoda is travelling to the planet Dagobah. He will be safely hidden there, until such time as the tide turns in our favour once again. Obi-Wan has arrived on Tatooine and travelled to the home of Owen and Beru Lars. They will bring Luke up, protecting him from the notice of the Sith.

And here on Alderaan, I have given my wife our beautiful baby daughter, Leia. We have agreed that it is best she knows nothing of her heritage. For now, we can only raise these children in secret, and hope that one day they will be strong enough to challenge the Sith and bring about the return of the Jedi.

MESSAGE RECORDING 20068

NAME: HAN SOLO

LOCATION: TATOOINE

It was not my fault! How many times am I gonna have to say it? EVERYONE gets boarded sometimes, and for that, Jabba the Hutt wants my head on a plate. Anyhow, I'm well out of Tatooine.

It all started when I was sitting minding my own business in the Mos Eisley cantina, keeping my head down because I knew Jabba's underlings would be looking for me. Chewie was at the bar and I saw him chattering away to some old guy who looked like a cross between a hermit and monk. I didn't pay too much attention – until the old guy pulled out a lightsaber and cut off the arm of the sidekick of that idiot who's always boasting that he's wanted in twelve systems.

Next thing you know, Chewie's introducing me to this weirdo, who's looking for passage to the Alderaan system. I told them that the *Millennium Falcon* was my ship, and would you believe, they'd never even heard of it! Anyway, this old guy and his friend, some overeager kid called Luke Skywalker, were willing to pay a ridiculous amount of money for me to take them to Alderaan. I'm not one to look a gift horse in the mouth, and besides, if I'm ever gonna be able to walk around on Tatooine again, I needed a way to pay Jabba back what I owe him.

They headed off and I was about to do the same when that slimeball Greedo turned up, pointing a gun at me and looking as smug as anyone who has a trunk for a face can look. He started spouting a speech about how I should have paid Jabba when I had the chance and how it was too late for me now. He was just itching for a reason to pull the trigger. I slowly reached for my gun under the table – I knew I didn't have much time. His trigger finger moved – but mine was faster. He was still smoking when I left the cantina and flipped the bartender a few coins to make up for the mess.

When I got to the docking bay, Jabba was waiting for me. I just about managed to talk him into giving me a little more time to pay him back – Jabba appreciates someone who'll talk back to him. Whimpering and begging never works with a Hutt.

I thought that escaping Jabba meant that the worst of it was over with, which just goes to show how wrong a person can be. Before we were even aboard the *Falcon*, stormtroopers piled into the docking bay and started firing on us. I took off and started to make the calculations for the jump to light speed. The kid was panicking, Chewie was wailing and the protocol droid with them was wittering on about how much he hates space travel. I've got a really wacko bunch of passengers this time, all right!

MESSAGE RECORDING 20080

NAME: PRINCESS LEIA

LOCATION: MASSASSI OUTPOST, YAVIN 4

Vader had tortured me in every despicable way he could think of, but he hadn't reckoned with me before. There was no way I was going to betray my friends. When we reached Alderaan, Governor Tarkin took over. He told me to reveal the location of the Rebel base or my home planet would be destroyed.

I had to think fast. I couldn't reveal the location of the Rebel base, but neither could I allow them to kill all those innocent people. I eventually told them about the Rebel base on Dantooine, which has been deserted for some time now.

That was when they showed how heartless they really are. Even though I had answered their question, they blew up my beautiful Alderaan anyway, killing my people and my family. I wanted to die myself, it hurt so much.

When they found out that I had lied to them, they condemned me to death and I was placed in a detention cell to await execution.

MESSAGE RECORDING 20079

NAME: C-3PO

LOCATION: MASSASSI OUTPOST, YAVIN 4

Master Kenobi left us to try to disable the tractor beam. As he left he looked at Master Luke and said, 'The Force will be with you, always'. It sounded rather final.

As we were waiting for the tractor beam to be disabled, Artoo-Deetoo whistled and beeped as if his life depended on it. Princess Leia was on board!

As soon as he heard the news, Master Luke refused to leave without trying to rescue her – she was about to be executed! Master Luke came up with a plan, which involved him, Master Solo and Chewbacca going to the detention area! Artoo and I were ordered to stay in the command office, lock the door and hope the stormtroopers didn't have blasters. I'm afraid it wasn't a very reassuring plan.

Artoo and I hid in a supply cabinet, and we heard a great explosion, which was presumably the door of the command office being blasted across the room. The next moment the door of the supply cabinet opened and a stormtrooper was staring at us.

I pretended that I was a space station droid, and told the officers that the intruders were heading for the prison level. We raced to the nearest terminal and Artoo plugged himself in to the main computer. I was just hoping that we were going to be in time!

The rescue team and Princess Leia were caught in a garbage room, and they were only a few seconds away from being crushed! Artoo managed to shut down the mashers in time.

We made it to the main hangar and waited for the others to arrive. The whole space station was searching for us by this time and troops

were milling around the entry ramp of the *Millennium Falcon* – I could not imagine how we were going to get away.

Suddenly, I realised that all the troops were looking one way. In a hallway just off the hangar bay, Master Kenobi and Darth Vader were duelling, their lightsabers flashing. As we used the distraction to run to the ship, Master Kenobi held up his lightsaber and closed his eyes. It was almost as if he was accepting his destiny. Darth Vader struck Master Kenobi down and his body *vanished*.

There was no time to wonder what had happened – we had to escape. I will say this for Master Solo – he may be impulsive, but he knows how to fly. The *Millennium Falcon* powered away from the space station and rocketed off into space. We came under attack from several fighters, but Master Luke and Master Solo managed to destroy them all. We headed for Yavin 4, the headquarters of the Rebellion.

QUIZ

Part Four

ANSWER THESE QUESTIONS ABOUT THE FIRST VICTORY OF THE REBELLION AND ADD YOUR SCORE TO YOUR TOTAL FROM PARTS 1–3.

QUESTION 1

Who was Owen Lars' stepmother?

shmi skywalker

QUESTION 2

What was Luke's comm-unit designation in the Battle of Yavin?

red five

QUESTION 3

Which bounty hunter tried to kill Han Solo?

Greedo

were milling around the entry ramp of the *Millennium Falcon* – I could not imagine how we were going to get away.

Suddenly, I realised that all the troops were looking one way. In a hallway just off the hangar bay, Master Kenobi and Darth Vader were duelling, their lightsabers flashing. As we used the distraction to run to the ship, Master Kenobi held up his lightsaber and closed his eyes. It was almost as if he was accepting his destiny. Darth Vader struck Master Kenobi down and his body *vanished*.

There was no time to wonder what had happened – we had to escape. I will say this for Master Solo – he may be impulsive, but he knows how to fly. The *Millennium Falcon* powered away from the space station and rocketed off into space. We came under attack from several fighters, but Master Luke and Master Solo managed to destroy them all. We headed for Yavin 4, the headquarters of the Rebellion.

MESSAGE RECORDING 20086

NAME: PRINCESS LEIA

LOCATION: MASSASSI OUTPOST, YAVIN 4

With the plans that we had managed to steal, the Rebels know that the Death Star has one weakness, but the target area is only two metres wide. A precise hit on the thermal exhaust port will destroy the entire battle station. However, it will take an exceptional pilot to make that shot. As we listened to General Dodonna explaining the difficulties in the war briefing room, the star pilots were looking very solemn. Only Luke seems confident that it can be done.

That arrogant Han Solo and his walking carpet of a friend were standing at the back of the room, listening, although I don't know why. Han made it crystal clear that all he is interested in is money. And why should I care about what a scoundrel like that is interested in, anyway? As far as I'm concerned, the sooner he leaves, the better.

I said goodbye to Luke as he prepared to pilot one of the fighters with my brave little Artoo-Deetoo. It was strangely emotional; although I have only known him a short time, I feel as if we have known each other for years.

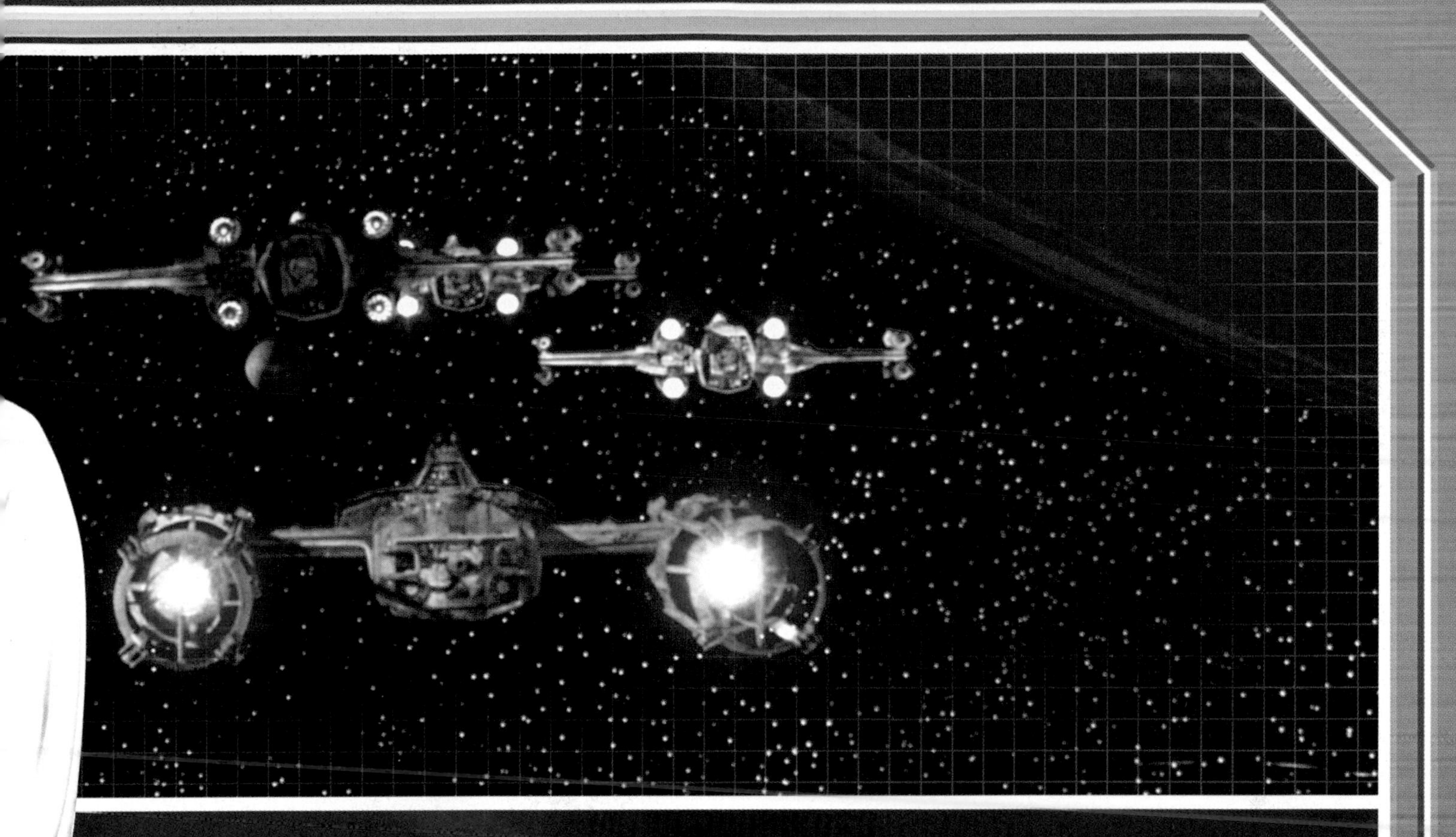

MESSAGE RECORDING 20087

NAME: PRINCESS LEIA

LOCATION: MASSASSI OUTPOST, YAVIN 4

As the final preparations were made for the approaching battle, the hangar was buzzing with the last-minute activity. I went to the war room and joined the field commander before the giant display, which showed the Death Star and would soon show our fighters. The war room buzzed with a din of chatter, but all my attention was on the screen as our Rebel pilots sped into space to engage the Imperial enemy.

As our pilots engaged the enemy and the battle began, the atmosphere in the war room was electric. We followed the battle on our comm-unit and on the display, my heart racing with every attack, every hit. As laserbolts streaked and fireballs exploded, our fighters repeatedly tried to hit the tiny target, but each attempt failed. Darth Vader himself was flying one of the Imperial fighters, and he was hot on the tail of any fighter that targeted the exhaust port. Rebel pilot after Rebel pilot failed and crashed. I was barely breathing as again and again our hopes were dashed.

With only a minute left before the Death Star would be in range to destroy Yavin 4, Luke prepared to try. He was now our only hope. But Darth Vader was on his tail, and he had destroyed the pilots who were supposed to be protecting Luke.

Luke's ship streaked through the trench of the Death Star, hurtling towards the exhaust port, his computer preparing the target . . . and then suddenly Luke switched off the targeting computer! He said that he was all right, but despair clutched at all of us – how could he hope to hit the port?

A large burst of Vader's laserfire engulfed Artoo-Deetoo and his beeping sounds died out. I could feel See-Threepio look at me, but there was no time to comfort him. The Death Star was now within range to blow us to smithereens and Vader was in position to destroy Luke. Then suddenly, one of Vader's wingmen was destroyed. It was Han! He hadn't abandoned us after all! As soon as he turned up, the tide turned in our favour. Vader's wingmen panicked and crashed, and Vader's damaged ship spun out of control, heading for deep space.

I should have had more faith in Luke. He was allowing the Force to flow through him, and that is more powerful than any targeting computer. Luke sent his photon torpedoes straight into the target using the power of the Force. The Death Star exploded into millions of tiny burning pieces!

Artoo-Deetoo has been repaired and is as good as new. Best of all, the Rebellion has delivered its first real blow to the Empire. Cheered by the Rebel troops, I gave medals to Luke, Chewbacca and Han. Together they have filled us with new hope that the Empire can one day be destroyed.

FACT FILES

LUKE SKYWALKER'S FIRST BATTLE

Luke Skywalker learned to fly in his T-16 skyhopper on Tatooine, along with his close friend Biggs Darklighter. When he arrived at the Rebel base on Yavin 4, Biggs Darklighter vouched for his skills and got Luke to join the Battle of Yavin as Red Five.

Fortunately, the T-16 and the T-65B X-wing (both manufactured by Incom) had similar control systems and handling characteristics, so Luke was able to adapt to the starfighter quickly.

Despite Luke's abilities, he was not a trained fighter pilot and before he gained his reputation as a skilled pilot, he lost no fewer than four X-wings. The first was lost the day after the Battle of Yavin, when Luke encountered a stray TIE fighter that had survived the battle. Not long afterwards, Luke crashed an X-wing on Mimban after flying into a severe electrical storm.

Another X-wing survived a crash landing on Dagobah, only to be abandoned on Bespin after the Empire took over Cloud City. Almost immediately after Luke's recovery from his duel with Darth Vader, he lost yet another X-wing when he encountered a Rebel corvette that had been taken over by Special Probe Droid 13-K.

Luke eventually had much better luck with an X-wing AA-589. He flew that particular X-wing for so long that R2-D2 developed a near-counterpart relationship with the ship.

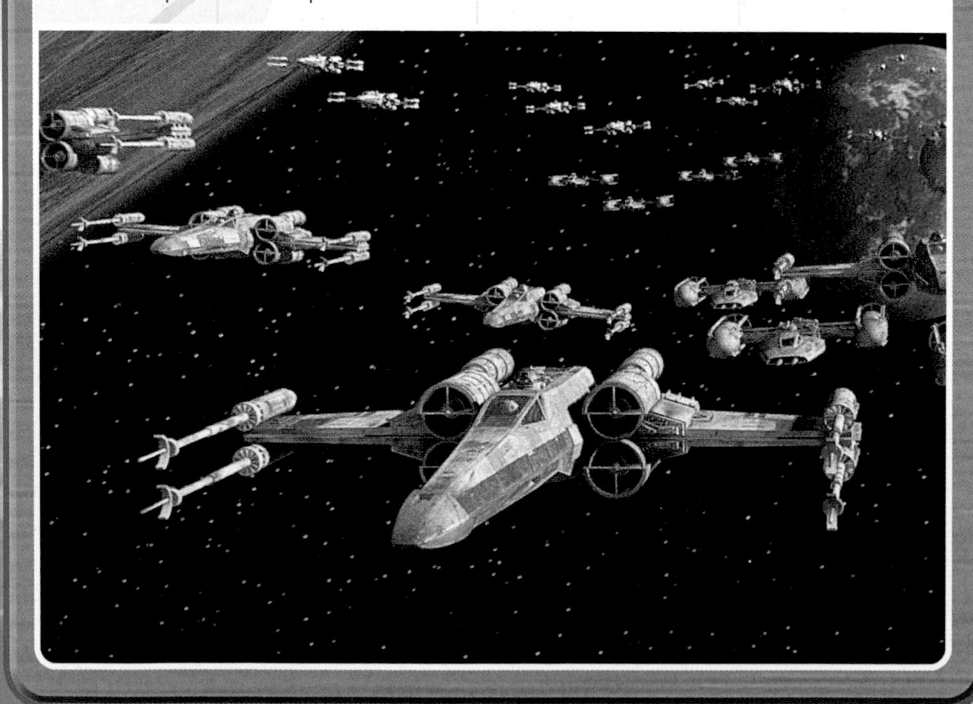

THE DEATH STAR PLANS

The Geonosians had the schematics for this ultimate weapon during the Battle of Geonosis. They gave the plans to Count Dooku, and those plans ultimately fell into the hands of Governor Tarkin.

The Death Star was intended to finally crush the Rebellion while spreading fear throughout the galaxy. It was constructed in secret near a penal colony, and it housed the destructive superlaser, which was used to completely obliterate the peaceful world of Alderaan.

A Rebel mercenary, Kyle Katarn, stole the Death Star plans from an Imperial data vault on Danuta. He transmitted these plans to Rebel spies in the Toprawa system. The plans were combined with similar technical data secured by Keyan Farlander to construct a full schematic of the Death Star.

Bria Tharen and her Red Hand Squadron received the Death Star schematics when they were transmitted to Toprawa, and beamed them to Princess Leia Organa aboard the *Tantive IV*.

YAVIN 4

Yavin 4 is a moon orbiting the gas giant Yavin. It is a hot jungle world with four main continents separated by six oceans, and one landlocked sea. Volcanic mountain ranges and wide rivers can be found amid the thick jungles and towering, purple-barked Massassi trees. The moon has both a wet and dry season, and storms whip across its surface every few months.

It was originally settled by a Dark Lord of the Sith, Naga Sadow, and his minions. Over time, the survivors of Sadow's people evolved into the deadly Massassi Warriors, who built dramatic temples throughout the jungles of Yavin 4 before they vanished into legend.

Yavin 4's plant life includes sense-enhancing blueleaf shrubs, climbing ferns, feather ferns, colorful nebula orchids, blistering touch-not shrubs and explosive grenade fungi. Jungle life is varied and ranges from semi-intelligent simians called woolamanders to mucous salamanders and purple jumping spiders. Yavinian runyips, lizard crabs, swimming crabs, whisper birds, reptile birds, stinger lizards, crystal snakes, armored eels, stump lizards, crawlfish, ravenous stintaril rodents, tree ticks, spiderlike anglers, piranha beetles, and flying, two-headed reptiles also inhabit the planet.

JAWAS

Jawas are small, foul-smelling humanoids native to Tatooine, where they scavenge the deserts in search of lost droids, crashed starships or discarded junk. Jawas wear long, brown robes with large hoods, which leave only their bright, glowing eyes visible. They travel the wastes in giant sandcrawlers and speak in a barely intelligible gibberish. Jawas make frequent visits to moisture farms and larger settlements, such as Mos Espa, to sell their wares.

Jawas live in tight clans. Each sandcrawler can hold up to 300 clan members as well as the droids and other machinery that the creatures scavenge, repair and sell. The most prominent member of each clan is the shaman, a female who, the clan believes, has the ability to predict the future.

As food and water are scarce on Tatooine, the Jawas have learned to siphon water from the funnel flower and eat the hubba gourd, a difficult-to-digest fruit. Scientists believe that Jawas evolved from rodents, and progressed to standing upright by reaching for lichens and fungi that grow on underground cave walls.

ANSWER THESE QUESTIONS ABOUT THE FIRST VICTORY OF THE REBELLION AND ADD YOUR SCORE TO YOUR TOTAL FROM PARTS 1–3.

QUESTION 1

Who was Owen Lars' stepmother?

shmi skywalker ....

QUESTION 2

What was Luke's comm-unit designation in the Battle of Yavin?

red five ....

QUESTION 3

Which bounty hunter tried to kill Han Solo?

B Greedo ....

QUESTION 4

What was the name of Han Solo's ship?

millium falcon

QUESTION 5

Who dismantled the tractor beam that held Han's ship in the Death Star?

Obi - Wan

QUESTION 6

Where did Princess Leia tell Governor Tarkin the Rebels were based?

Dantooine

QUESTION 7

Which friend of Luke's was killed during the Battle of Yavin?

Biggs Darklighter

QUESTION 8

What do Wookiees sometimes do to their opponents when they lose?

Pull peoples arms out of their sockets

QUESTION 9

Whose voice advised Luke to use the Force during the Battle of Yavin?

Obi-Wan

QUESTION 10

Why did Leia kiss Luke in the Death Star?

For luck

PART 4 SCORE

10 out of 10

MESSAGE RECORDING 20547

NAME: PRINCESS LEIA

LOCATION: HOTH

I am recording this because there is a chance we won't come out of the next few hours alive, and some record has to be preserved of the bravery of the Rebel forces and the cruelty of the Emperor's tyrannous reign. Since the Death Star was destroyed three years ago, Imperial troops have pursued us across the galaxy. We established a new secret base here on Hoth, thinking that we would be safe on this remote ice world for a time. However, Darth Vader seems to be hunting us down with more determination than I have ever known before.

For a short time we had felt safe and hidden, but that all changed when Luke and Han went out to the plain of Hoth to check for life readings. They were riding tauntauns and placing sensors, and had almost finished when Luke decided to check out a meteorite that had hit the ground nearby. Han went back to the base, and Luke carried on alone. He has changed so much from the boy I met three years ago. He is now the leader of our band of freedom fighters and has become an even more skilled pilot. However, I know he still yearns to learn more about the ways of the Jedi, and become like his father.

(Han, of course, hasn't changed a bit. He is still the same pig-headed, arrogant, stuck-up, half-witted nerf-herder that he always was, and now he seems to have got it into his head that I have *feelings* for him! I'd just as soon kiss a Wookiee! He declared that he had had

enough of helping the Rebels and was heading back to Tatooine like the selfish pig he is, and then he expected me to just fall into his arms!)

Anyway, Luke ran into trouble out there and Han went after him. (He may be an idiot, but he's a brave idiot, I'll give him that.) I stood by the entrance to our ice cave, waiting for a sign – any sign – that they were coming back. Nights on Hoth are freezing and all the patrols came back. Still there was no contact from Luke or Han, and eventually we had to close the shield doors. Everyone was scared stiff, certain that Luke and Han were both dead. Somehow, though, I just knew that Luke was alive. It was as if I could sense it.

Sure enough, the following day they were discovered. Luke had been attacked by a wampa and had collapsed in the snow, hallucinating and close to death. But Han found him and kept him warm until morning, when one of our patrols found them. Luke is going to be fine, but he was able to reveal that the meteorite had in fact been a probe, and that meant that the Empire knew our position. We had to leave the system.

We were preparing to evacuate when alarms sounded throughout the base. A fleet of Star Destroyers was coming out of hyperspace. We rerouted all power to the energy shield – we had to hold them until all transports were away. We prepared for ground assault and I briefed the pilots in the hangar.

The heavy transport ships each had two fighter escorts. The ion cannon fired several shots to make sure that any enemy ships would be out of the flight path. Until the transports escaped the Imperial fleet, the atmosphere in the command centre was very tense. I was trying to show no fear, but I knew we were all feeling the same. Hopefully we will all meet again at the rendezvous point.

A fierce and deadly battle is underway on the ground and Luke is right in the middle of it. I only hope that he is able to escape and that we will all see each other again.

MESSAGE RECORDING 20548

NAME: LUKE SKYWALKER

LOCATION: DAGOBAH

As I sat in the main hangar deck awaiting the order to engage, my head was a whirl of thoughts. I couldn't stop thinking about the vision I saw after I escaped from the wampa – Obi-Wan Kenobi appeared to me, telling to go to the Dagobah system and find Jedi Master Yoda. I was worried for Leia and for Han – what if I never saw them again?

Then a trench officer reported Imperial walkers heading our way, and suddenly all other thoughts left my head and my mind was clear. I had to focus on the present, and that meant protecting our base from the Imperial troops. Our fleet of snowspeeders accelerated away from the base at full throttle, heading towards the distant walkers.

I told my team to keep in tight formation and then gave the order for attack pattern delta. The cannons mounted on the walkers' heads fired at our speeders and snow and ice exploded all around them. Then a giant walker head swivelled and fired, striking a snowspeeder and sending it crashing down in a ball of flames.

I headed straight for the viewport of the walker, blasting away. An explosion hit the walker window, but did no harm. I roared up and over the war machine, realising that its armour was too strong for blasters.

Suddenly I had an idea. I ordered my team to use their harpoons and tow cables and go for the legs. It was our only chance of stopping them. Laser bolts and flak filled the air, creating a deadly obstacle course. I remembered Ben's advice and tried to use the Force to help me, but everything was happening so fast! We flew in tight formation towards the walker as explosions burst all around us.

Wedge's speeder raced through the legs of one of the monstrous walkers and he activated the harpoon, embedding it in one of the walker's legs. Then Wedge raced around the giant walker's feet, before detaching the cable. The tangled legs attempted a step, and then the giant Imperial walker crashed onto the icy ground, sending snow and metal pieces flying. I knew that the troops in the trenches would be cheering!

Suddenly my ship was rocked by a huge explosion and filled with smoke. Electrical sparks jumped around the cockpit; I had been hit! I made an emergency landing

and escaped the wrecked snowspeeder right before being crushed by a walker. Running beneath the monstrous machine, I fired my harpoon gun at the underbelly. Stray laser bolts whistled by my head as I climbed up the cable to the walker's hull, reaching a small hatch. I cut the solid metal hatch with my lightsaber, took a landmine from around my neck and threw it into the Imperial machine.

Then, as fast as I could, I lowered myself to the icy ground far below – crashing to the ground and losing consciousness for a few moments. When I opened my eyes, the walker's mechanical insides were spewing out every opening. The machine sat dead in its tracks, smoking.

I heard a familiar roar and looked up to see the *Millennium Falcon* racing above us, flying very close to the ground. Han was safe, and the evacuation was complete. I pelted towards my X-wing fighter, where Artoo was waiting. It was time to leave.

We sped away from the planet and soon it disappeared into the stars behind us. Now that the battle was over, my previous thoughts came flooding back, and suddenly I knew what I had to do. I took the fighter into a steep turn and set a new course. Artoo let off a volley of concerned beeps and whistles as I told him that we were going to the Dagobah system.

As we approached Dagobah, I started to feel nervous. My scanners weren't picking up any cities or technology – just massive life form readings. We moved closer to the planet and into a dense covering of cloud. All my scopes were dead and I couldn't see a thing. Then there was a cracking sound and a tremendous jolt as we crashed into a boggy lake.

Artoo is not a droid who keeps his opinions to himself, and he insists that coming to Dagobah was a very bad idea. I am starting to think that he may be right. I can just imagine what Han would say if he knew I had travelled to a remote planet because of something I saw in a hallucination. But it felt so real . . .

MESSAGE RECORDING 20600

NAME: HAN SOLO

LOCATION: TATOOINE

Explosions were cracking the ice roof of the hangar and Chewie seemed to have forgotten everything he ever knew about repairing a ship. Ground staff were being evacuated all around us and Luke was heading off to fight the Imperial troops . . . and I couldn't get the *Falcon* off the ground! Not to mention the fact that her highness was in one of her most argumentative moods – and just when I was trying to save her life. The command centre was a shambles, a mess of cracked walls and broken pipes billowing hot steam. As I ran in, part of the roof caved in. Leia and See-Threepio were beside a control board, risking their lives, and all she could say to me was 'Why are you still here?'

By the time I got them back to the hangar, the last transport ship had gone. There was only one thing to do – I had to take them in the *Falcon*. Chewie still hadn't got her working, but after I tinkered with the control panel the engine fired up all right and we shot out of the hangar and hurtled into the sky, closely followed by a Star Destroyer and four TIE fighters. That was when I realised that we were racing towards two bright, star-sized objects – two more Star Destroyers! Our deflector shield was down so our only chance was to outmanoeuvre them.

We managed to hold them off until we could prepare to make the jump to light speed . . . and that's when we found out that the hyperdrive motivator had been damaged. It was impossible to go to lightspeed! I really had no idea how we were going to get out of that one. Then we flew into an asteroid field, and I had an idea. They'd be crazy to follow us in there!

We turned into the asteroid storm and veered around massive asteroids, racing through the rain of rocks. The TIE fighters were still after us, but they were no match for the *Falcon's* agility and they were soon either pulverised or out of control in deep space. With See-Threepio in full panic meltdown, Chewie roaring and Leia firing insults at me, I skimmed the ship along the surface of an asteroid and dove into a huge crater. We raced down the tunnel-like crater until a small cave appeared on one side, and I scooted into it and stopped.

While Chewie started to fix the hyperdrive, I tried to help Leia pull a lever to re-engage the system – and got snapped at again. But this time there was something else in her voice – something less annoyed. I suddenly got the feeling that this wasn't the time to say the wrong thing. Hoping I didn't blow it, I took her hand and spoke softly,

trying to let her see that there was more to me than she thought. I pulled her towards me and she tried to resist, but not very hard – I kissed her like no one had ever kissed her before. When I stopped, she tried to work up some of her old indignation, but she was finding it hard to talk. I was about to kiss her again . . . and then See-Threepio appeared in the doorway blathering on about the reverse power flux coupling. The moment was spoiled.

We soon discovered that we had more trouble than we had anticipated. The asteroid cave was no cave – it was the stomach of a giant space slug and we were inside it! Imperial troops or no Imperial troops, we had to get out of there. We zoomed out between the monster's teeth and raced back into the deadly rain of the asteroid field. Then we crossed the path of the Star Destroyer *Avenger* and they started to fire on us. The hyperdrive still wasn't working, and we only had one chance. It was a long shot, but I diverted all power to the front shield and headed directly for the *Avenger's* bridge, racing low across the hull. Then, before they could guess at our plan, I cut all power and attached the *Falcon* to the side of the *Avenger*. I knew that standard Imperial procedure was to dump all the ship's rubbish before moving to lightspeed. When the rubbish floated away, we would be floating with it.

My old friend Lando Calrissian was living fairly nearby in Bespin's Cloud City. I knew that he couldn't be trusted, but also he had no love for the Empire and I hoped he would look after us for a while. As we detached from the *Avenger* and floated away with the rubbish, Leia shook her head, grinned and then kissed me. I guess I finally did something right . . .

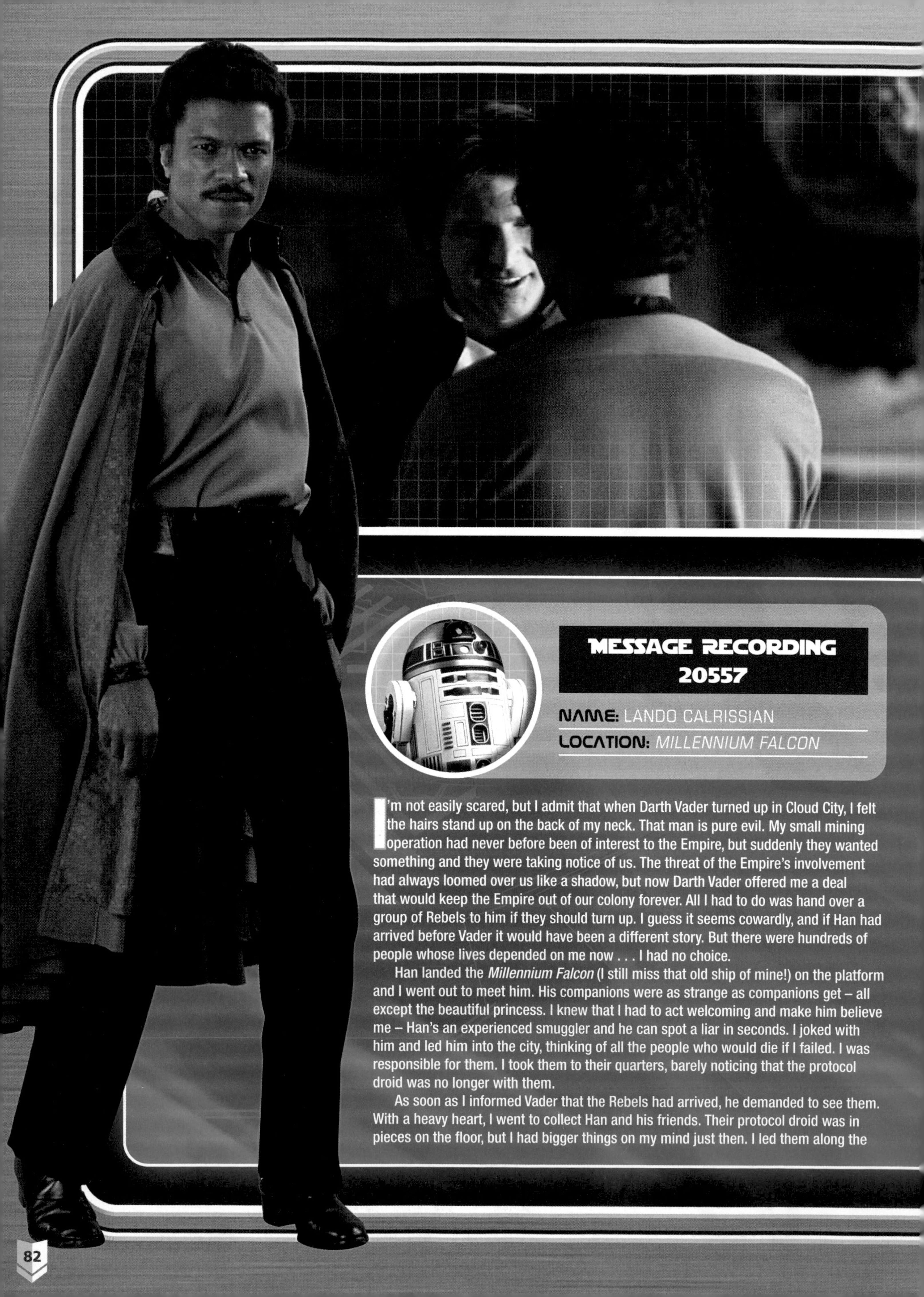

MESSAGE RECORDING 20557

NAME: LANDO CALRISSIAN

LOCATION: *MILLENNIUM FALCON*

I'm not easily scared, but I admit that when Darth Vader turned up in Cloud City, I felt the hairs stand up on the back of my neck. That man is pure evil. My small mining operation had never before been of interest to the Empire, but suddenly they wanted something and they were taking notice of us. The threat of the Empire's involvement had always loomed over us like a shadow, but now Darth Vader offered me a deal that would keep the Empire out of our colony forever. All I had to do was hand over a group of Rebels to him if they should turn up. I guess it seems cowardly, and if Han had arrived before Vader it would have been a different story. But there were hundreds of people whose lives depended on me now . . . I had no choice.

Han landed the *Millennium Falcon* (I still miss that old ship of mine!) on the platform and I went out to meet him. His companions were as strange as companions get – all except the beautiful princess. I knew that I had to act welcoming and make him believe me – Han's an experienced smuggler and he can spot a liar in seconds. I joked with him and led him into the city, thinking of all the people who would die if I failed. I was responsible for them. I took them to their quarters, barely noticing that the protocol droid was no longer with them.

As soon as I informed Vader that the Rebels had arrived, he demanded to see them. With a heavy heart, I went to collect Han and his friends. Their protocol droid was in pieces on the floor, but I had bigger things on my mind just then. I led them along the

corridor towards the room where Vader was waiting. Long shafts of light poured across the corridor. I started to tell Han my fears about the Empire – perhaps I was hoping that he might somehow guess what I was being forced to do. But then we reached the dining room and the doors slid open. Darth Vader was sitting at the far end of the banquet table, with that louse of a bounty hunter, Boba Fett, standing behind him. Han gave me a terrible look. I apologised, but even to my ears the words sounded hollow.

Chewbacca was locked in a cell with the pieces of the protocol droid. Meanwhile, Han was tortured while I stood by and listened to his screams. I listened as Vader told Boba Fett that he could take Han to Jabba the Hutt, as soon as he had lured Luke Skywalker here. Vader then told me that Leia and Chewbacca could never leave the city. At this, I had to speak my mind – these had never been conditions of our agreement. But Vader made it very clear that I had no option – either I had to agree, or he would leave a garrison of soldiers here to control the city. This deal was getting worse all the time.

The next thing that Vader wanted to see was the carbon-freezing chamber. He planned to freeze Luke Skywalker in there, but he decided to first test it out on Han. This could easily kill him. Leia and Chewbacca were brought to the chamber to watch, with the half-repaired protocol droid strapped to Chewbacca's back.

Han kissed Leia and walked to the hydraulic platform. As the platform dropped and Chewbacca howled, I felt physical pain course through my body. For me, it was a life-changing moment. I knew that I could no longer be a pawn of the Empire. When Han was brought out of the carbonite, I checked his life readings. To my relief, he had survived the freezing process and was now in perfect hibernation.

Luke Skywalker had just landed as Vader gave the orders to take Leia and Chewbacca to his ship. I might have known he would alter the deal. As we left the chamber, we saw young Skywalker enter it. Leia called out to him that it was a trap, but she was dragged away.

I had ordered my men to intercept us, and soon our stormtrooper guards were being locked up. I had to get Han's friends out of there – it was the least I owed him. Leia despised me and Chewie almost killed me, but finally I persuaded them to trust me. We were too late to save Han, but we could still reach the *Millennium Falcon*. Under heavy fire, I told the citizens of the city to evacuate and then we all headed for the landing platform. We made it on to the ship and roared away from the city, with TIE fighters in hot pursuit.

MESSAGE RECORDING 20549

NAME: MASTER YODA

LOCATION: DAGOBAH

When young Skywalker arrived on Dagobah, reluctant was I to take on his training. Impatient was he – reckless. There was much anger in him, like his father. He was not ready. However, Obi-Wan was very determined, and the boy was strong with the Force and eager to learn the ways of the Jedi. Old am I, and if the prophecy of the Chosen One is yet to come true, young Skywalker is our hope for the future.

A slow start he made in his training. Always his tasks were too hard, his mind too full of questions. He failed his tests because he had fear inside his heart, like his father before him. Always with him it could not be done. He could not understand that he had to unlearn everything he had learned. He could not believe in his own feelings, and that is why he failed.

Slowly, slowly, young Skywalker began to improve. He was learning to control his fear, to let the Force flow through him. But when he began to see through the Force, distressed he became. He saw friends in pain – visions of the future were they. At first I was able to persuade him not to run after them. I sensed that he would destroy all for which they had fought and suffered.

However, powerful was Skywalker's feeling for his friends. Determined was he to go to their aid. Obi-Wan too tried to stop him, by appearing in his human form.

All too aware were we of how vulnerable young Jedi can be. Their training is a dangerous time, when the dark side of the Force can tempt them.

Luke would not listen. Reckless and determined was he. He gave me his word that he would return to complete his training, but only a fully trained Jedi Knight with the Force as his ally will conquer Vader and his Emperor. I warned him that if he ended his training like this, he would be choosing the quick and easy path – he would be an agent of evil.

Luke is going to leave, no matter what Obi-Wan and I say. Many dangers await him. Unprepared is he to face Vader. Unprepared to know whom Vader really is. If we lose Luke to the dark side, only Leia will remain.

MESSAGE RECORDING 20550

NAME: LUKE SKYWALKER

LOCATION: EN ROUTE TO CLOUD CITY

I could not keep the vision of Leia and Han suffering out of my head – I could not let them die because of me. I know I can help them – I can feel the Force flowing through me! Obi-Wan appeared to me and told me that if I choose to face Vader, he cannot interfere – I will be alone. A battle raged in my mind, but in the end I had to listen to my heart. I will remember what I have learned and I will not turn to the dark side, but I cannot let my friends be sacrificed for me.

I know where I have to go – Bespin's shining city in the clouds. Vader awaits me there – I can feel it.

MESSAGE RECORDING 20560

NAME: LUKE SKYWALKER

LOCATION: REBEL CRUISER

When I entered the carbon-freezing chamber, the room was deathly quiet and full of steam. Then I saw a dark figure standing on a walkway above me. It was Vader, and he taunted me. I ignited my lightsaber and in an instant, Vader's own red lightsaber was alight. I lunged forward, eager to engage my enemy. Again and again our blades clashed and hummed in battle.

I drove him back, surprising him with my abilities. But I was guilty of arrogance, because next moment Vader hooked my lightsaber out of my hand and sent it flying through the air. I had to jump back to protect myself, and I lost my balance and fell down the stairs to the carbon-freezing platform. Vader tried to tell me that my destiny lied with him.

We fought again, but I was more cautious this time. I remembered what Yoda had said about controlling my anger. Our duel raged as the room continued to fill up with steam. Vader used the Force to send large pieces of machinery hurtling towards me. I did my best to deflect everything, but soon I was bloodied and bruised. Finally, one machine smashed through the large window and a fierce wind blew into the room.

I fell on to the gantry and our lightsabers met again in a vicious battle. I backed away off along the narrow end of the gantry as Vader came at me. Then his lightsaber sliced off my hand and sent my lightsaber flying. In agony, I squeezed my forearm under my left armpit and moved along to the extreme end of the gantry. There was nowhere else to go.

At that desperate moment, Vader told me something that tore me apart. He is my father! I longed to believe that he was lying, but my feelings told me it was the truth. As I reeled from this news, Vader asked me to join him – he said that we could rule the galaxy as father and son.

A great sense of peace and calm descended on me. The strength of the Force entered me, and I knew that I would rather die than join the dark side. I stepped off the gantry platform into space, falling through the darkness and unable to grab on to anything to break my fall.

As I tumbled past an electronic weather vane, I hooked one of my legs around the fragile instruments. In that instant, something told me to call for Leia. I concentrated all my remaining energy on reaching her, willing her to hear me. There was an ominous cracking sound from the base of the weather vane and a piece broke off, falling into the clouds far below. I was nearly unconscious, hanging upside-down on the weather vane as my body shifted in the wind. I slipped and started to fall – but Leia had heard me and had come to the rescue I tumbled into the hatch of the *Millennium Falcon*.

As the others tried to escape Vader's fighters, I felt broken and beaten. I could sense that Vader's ship was very near. Using the Force, my father called to me. Why did no one tell me who he really was? What happened to Anakin Skywalker all those years ago?

We have reached the Rebel cruiser, and I am feeling stronger and more able to control my feelings. Lando, Leia and I have developed a plan to rescue Han, and when the time comes we will rendezvous on Tatooine. But for now, I must find a way to complete my training. Sometime soon I will have to face my father again.

MESSAGE RECORDING 20563

NAME: C-3PO

LOCATION: REBEL CRUISER

This has been one of the worst days of my existence so far, and with all I've been through, that really is saying something. Master Han has been frozen in carbonite and taken off to goodness knows where. I have been taken apart and used as a plaything, and then half put back together the wrong way round and strapped to the back of that woolly Wookiee. And as if that wasn't enough, Darth Vader wants us all dead! Oh my circuits, I have been shot at more in the last few hours than ever before in my existence!

After we left Cloud City, Lando's idea was to get as far away from Darth Vader as possible, and I wholeheartedly agreed with his plan. But then Princess Leia declared that we had to turn back! She somehow knew where Master Luke was, and thank the maker, we were able to rescue him. But our adventures still weren't over. The hyperdrive had been deactivated and Lord Vader's TIE fighters were chasing our ship. Artoo was supposed to be putting me back together, but suddenly he rushed off to a control panel, leaving me standing in pieces, without a word of explanation! I admit that he did manage to fix the hyperdrive and we were able to escape, but I still say it was more by luck than judgement. (Artoo is definitely having delusions of grandeur.)

Lando has taken the *Millennium Falcon* to search for Master Solo, and there seems to be a plan afoot to return to Tatooine. I only hope they don't want me to get mixed up in any more adventures!

THE REBEL ALLIANCE

The Alliance to Restore the Republic was a valiant band of freedom fighters who joined together to oppose the tyranny of Emperor Palpatine. Rogue Imperial Senators founded the group in the early days of the Emperor's rule. When it became clear that Palpatine intended to dominate the universe, entire planets and systems joined the Alliance's cause.

In early days, the leaders of the resistance tried to act against the Empire in secret. Eventually, Emperor Palpatine discovered them and former Senators such as Mon Mothma and Garm Bel Iblis were forced to flee for their lives. Mon Mothma, Iblis and Bail Organa met on Corellia to formally establish the Rebellion. They drafted the Declaration to Restore the Republic, which founded the Alliance.

The ranks of the Alliance were soon swelled joined by hundreds of pilots, soldiers, technicians and officers who wished to see the Empire fall.

REBEL PILOTS

Rebel pilots wore orange and white jumpsuits, personalised helmets and tool belts, and they were trained to fly virtually all Rebel craft. Most flew X-wings or Y-wings during space combat. Only the exceptionally skilful pilots were commissioned for B-wing duty, while the most courageous stepped into the cockpit of the lightly armoured A-wing. The pilots also mastered snowspeeders and a host of large starships, ranging from Nebulon-B frigates to Gallofree Yards transports.

Although they came from a diverse range of worlds, all were idealistic and willing to sacrifice their lives for the Alliance. This unfaltering courage was to lead to several crucial victories for the Alliance.

Rebel Alliance fighters were organised into squadrons of twelve fighters each. Each starfighter base had at least one squadron, but several bases had four or more. Each Squadron adopted an emblem, and every pilot wore his helmet as a symbol of loyalty and pride.

REBEL FIGHTER FACTS

- **There were thirty-six starfighters in a wing, under the control of one wing commander.**
- **There were three squadrons per wing. A squadron consisted of twelve starfighters.**
- **Each squadron was broken down into three flights with four starfighters per flight.**
- **The smallest tactical unit consisted of two starfighters, a leader and a wingmate.**
- **Red rank insignias indicated an Army designation. Blue rank insignias indicated a Navy designation.**

RANKS IN ALLIANCE SPECIAL FORCES

SpecForce Rank	Command Level	Alliance Army	Alliance Navy
General	Division	General	Admiral
Colonel	Regiment	Colonel	Captain
Major	Regiment or Co.	Major	Commander
Captain	Co. or Platoon	Captain	Lieutenant
Senior Lieutenant	Platoon	Lieutenant	Lieutenant
Lieutenant	Platoon	Lieutenant	Ensign
Master Sergeant	Platoon 2nd	Sergeant Major	Chief Petty Officer
Sergeant	Squad	Sergeant	Petty Officer
Senior Trooper	Fire team	Senior Trooper	Senior Deckman
Trooper	-	Trooper	Deckman

QUIZ

Part Five

ANSWER THESE QUESTIONS ABOUT THE ALLIANCE'S BATTLES WITH THE EMPIRE AND ADD YOUR SCORE TO YOUR TOTAL FROM PARTS 1–4.

QUESTION 1

Which ice creature attacked Luke on Hoth?

Wompa

QUESTION 2

In which ship did Princess Leia escape from Hoth?

QUESTION 3

Why did Luke go to Dagobah?

to Learn the ways of the force

QUESTION 4

Which creature did Han kill when the *Millennium Falcon* was inside the giant space slug?

Mynock

QUESTION 5

What did Luke see inside the dark cave on Dagobah?

vision of Darth Vader

QUESTION 6

Whose head did the Ugnaughts play with in the Cloud City junk room?

C-3PO's head

QUESTION 7

How many questions was Han asked when he was tortured in Cloud City?

None

QUESTION 8

What was Han's reply when Princess Leia first told him that she loved him?

'I know'

QUESTION 9

Who took Han to Jabba the Hutt?

Boba Fett

QUESTION 10

Where did Luke agree to rendezvous with Lando to find Han?

Tatooine

PART 5 SCORE

10 out of 10

MESSAGE RECORDING 20582

NAME: C-3PO

LOCATION: TATOOINE

Of course, it was too much to expect that this beeping blue droid wouldn't involve me in any more madcap adventures. No, I had to return to this beastly, sandy planet with him and now I'm up to my neck in trouble – again.

Lando Calrissian and Chewbacca had never returned from Jabba the Hutt's palace, where they had gone to search for Master Solo. That's why Artoo and I were hurrying along a lonely, windswept road on Tatooine. I was terribly worried – if Artoo knew half the things I've heard about Jabba the Hutt, he'd probably short circuit. We arrived at the massive gates and knocked. I was hoping that there was no one at home, but the gates were opened and my stubby companion scooted inside. Why does he always have to rush into things without thinking them through?

I told Jabba's guard that we were bringing a message, and then Artoo piped up and added that we also had a gift. I should have known there and then that things were going to get unpleasant. Soon we were standing in front of the monarch of the galactic underworld, and he certainly was every bit as repulsive as I had always been told. I bowed and told Artoo to play Master Luke's message. This is what he had recorded:

Greetings, Exalted One. Allow me to introduce myself. I am Luke Skywalker, Jedi Knight and friend to Captain Solo. I know that you are powerful, mighty Jabba, and that your anger with Solo must be equally powerful. I seek an audience with Your Greatness to bargain for Solo's life. With your wisdom, I'm sure that we can work out an arrangement which will be mutually beneficial and enable us to avoid any unpleasant confrontation. As a token of my goodwill, I present to you a gift: these two droids. Both are hard

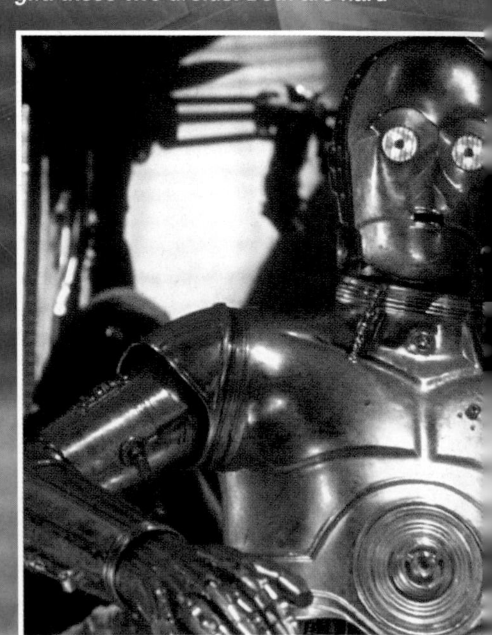

working and will serve you well.

Well! I could hardly believe my sound processors. Jabba just laughed at Master Luke's message. He has no intention of giving up his favourite decoration – Master Solo is still frozen in carbonite and hanging on Jabba's wall! And now we are at Jabba's mercy. I have been put to work as an interpreter and Artoo has been sent to Jabba's sail barge.

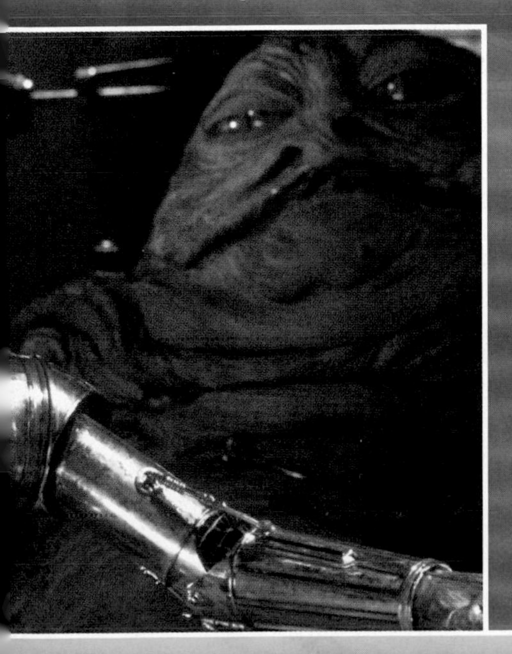

Jabba's court is a terrible place. Soon after I arrived, he fed one of his dancers to a monster beneath the floor, just because she wouldn't sit next to him! Everyone in the court was laughing hysterically when a gunshot rang out. There was a commotion on the far side of the room and then an odd-looking bounty hunter led Chewbacca into the room. It was my unhappy job to translate Jabba's words. The bounty hunter argued with Jabba over the price, and eventually threatened to blow us all to smithereens. Thankfully Jabba seemed to find this amusing, although I cannot imagine why. Chewbacca was handed over and the party started again. As Chewbacca was led away I spotted the one of the skiff guards was Lando Calrissian! Perhaps Master Luke has a plan after all.

MESSAGE RECORDING 20583

NAME: PRINCESS LEIA

LOCATION: *MILLENNIUM FALCON*

At first everything seemed to be going smoothly – everyone had been fooled by my disguise as the bounty hunter. But when I tried to rescue Han, I was caught and chained to Jabba like a slave. Han was dragged away and I knew that he would be taken to join Chewbacca. I hadn't had time to explain anything to him – he didn't even know about Luke's training, or the fact that he is now a Jedi Knight!

I knew that it would not be long before Luke came to rescue us. Sure enough, Luke used an old Jedi mind trick on one of Jabba's weak-minded servants and soon he was standing in front of the foul gangster.

Luke tried to bargain with Jabba, but the Hutt would not listen. He threw Luke into the rancor pit, and for a moment I was worried, but then I caught Lando's eye and he shook his head at me. This was obviously all part of the plan. Sure enough, Luke managed to kill the monster and a startled gasp rose from the court. Jabba was actually turning red with anger. I couldn't hide my delight!

My friends were sentenced to death and taken out to the pit of Carkoon, the nesting place of the Sarlacc. As he stood above the pit, Luke offered Jabba one last chance to live, but of course the gangster just laughed at him. However, he wasn't laughing for much longer. Luke looked up at Artoo and gave him a funny little salute: the signal the little droid had been waiting for. A flap opened in his domed head and he catapulted Luke's lightsaber towards him. Moving with such skill and speed as I have never seen, Luke fought off the guards and untied Han and Chewbacca.

At that moment, the deck gunmen on the barge unleashed a series of blasts and Lando was thrown from the deck of the skiff. He managed to grab a rope, and dangled above the Sarlacc pit.

At the same time, Boba Fett ignited his rocket pack, leaped into the air and flew from the barge down to the skiff. He aimed his laser gun at Luke, but Luke just spun around and hacked his gun in half. Boba fired a cable out of his armoured sleeve, pinning his arms against his side, but Luke used his lightsaber to cut the wire and free himself.

Another blast from the barge's deck gun knocked Boba out. Luke leaped on to the second skiff and began fighting guards. As Boba woke up, my poor Han, still blind, scrabbled around for a weapon and grasped a spear. As Boba Fett raised his arm to attack, Han hit his rocket pack with the spear. Boba was blasted across the skiff like a missile, smashing against the side of the sail barge and sliding away into the pit. He screamed as he hurtled into the mouth of the Sarlacc.

I couldn't bear to stand there and do nothing any longer. I turned to Jabba and threw my chain around his neck. Then I dived off the other side of the throne, pulling the chain as hard as I could. His huge eyes bulged from their sockets and his scum-coated tongue flopped out. At last his foul body shook in a final spasm, and he died.

Outside, Han had pulled Lando back up to the skiff. Luke was now on board the sail barge, cutting down the gunners. Artoo rushed up to me and cut my chain. We raced for the exit, grabbing See-Threepio on the way. Up on deck, Luke was battling with the guards. I climbed on to the platform of the barge cannon and pointed it at the floor. The droids jumped down to the sand below and Luke ran towards me. He had one of the rigging ropes from the mast around one arm, and he grabbed me with the other. Then he kicked the trigger of the deck gun and the deck exploded as we swung out towards the skiff. As the sail barge exploded, we zoomed away towards the *Millennium Falcon.*

MESSAGE RECORDING 20586

NAME: LUKE SKYWALKER

LOCATION: IMPERIAL SHUTTLE, DESTINATION THE FOREST MOON OF ENDOR

The Alliance was assembled and I had to join Han, Lando and Leia at the fleet, but first I had to keep my promise to Master Yoda and return to Dagobah. In Yoda's cottage, a warm yellow light was illuminating the room.

Yoda was very, very old, and he knew that he did not have very long to live. He was tired, and was looking forward to resting. That is the way of things . . . the way of the Force.

Master Yoda has made it clear that I am not yet a Jedi. One thing remains: Vader. I must confront him. This knowledge is agony. I told Master Yoda that I know Vader is my father.

Master Yoda felt that it was unfortunate that I had rushed to face him without completing my training. He told me to remember that a Jedi's strength flows from the Force, but that anger, fear and aggression are the paths to the dark side.

He weakened as he talked, warning me not to underestimate the powers of the Emperor. He said that the Force runs strong in my family, and I must pass on what I have learned. With his last breath, Master Yoda revealed that there is another Skywalker. Then a shiver ran through his body and he died. Just as Obi-Wan had done, Master Yoda disappeared.

I went slowly back to my ship, feeling scared and lonely. I am now the last of the Jedi, and at that moment it seemed impossible to go on alone. But then I heard a voice telling me that Yoda would always be with me, and when I looked up I saw the shimmering image of Obi-Wan Kenobi.

My first reaction was to demand the truth – to ask why he had failed to tell me who my father really is. Obi-Wan told me that father ceased to be Anakin Skywalker and became Darth Vader. When that happened, the good man who was my father was destroyed. Obi-Wan believes that my father is more machine now than man – twisted and evil. But I can't kill my own father.

Obi-Wan told me that the other Skywalker Master Yoda spoke of is my twin sister. To protect us both from the Emperor, we were hidden from our father when we were born. The Emperor knew that any children of Anakin would be a threat to him. As soon as Obi-Wan said this, my insight told me the truth. Leia is my sister!

I must bury my feelings deep down, for now. They could be made to serve the Emperor.

I left Dagobah and sped towards the Rebel fleet. It was so vast that it stretched as far as the eye could see. A dozen small Corellian battleships were flying overhead in formation. Fighters and battlecruisers surrounded the largest of the Rebel star cruisers, the headquarters frigate. I docked and hurried towards the main briefing room, where a final briefing was in progress.

The Death Star is orbiting the forest moon of Endor, and the Emperor himself is personally overseeing the final stages of construction. Although the weapon systems on this Death Star are not yet operational, the Death Star is protected by an energy shield, which is generated from the forest moon of Endor. The shield must be deactivated if any attack is to be attempted. Once the shield is down, our cruisers will create a perimeter, while the fighters fly into the superstructure and attempt to knock out the main reactor.

Lando, who is now a general, has volunteered to lead the fighter attack. We have stolen a small Imperial shuttle. Disguised as a cargo ship, and using a secret Imperial code, a strike team will land on the moon and deactivate the shield generator. Han, who is also now a general, is going to lead the strike team. Leia, Chewie and I will be going with him.

Lando is going to take the *Millennium Falcon*. We all said our goodbyes in the docking bay and headed up the ramp into the Imperial shuttle. Everything now depends on our team deactivating the shield generator.

MESSAGE RECORDING 20590

NAME: HAN SOLO

LOCATION: EWOK VILLAGE, FOREST MOON OF ENDOR

As we left the docking bay, I couldn't help but take a final look at the *Millennium Falcon*. I had a funny feeling that I wasn't going to see her again. I mean sure, this is the best chance we've had to destroy the Emperor, but the odds are still astronomical.

We managed to get past the Imperial deflector shield using a stolen clearance code and we were soon on our way to the Sanctuary Moon. Then Luke started getting jittery, suddenly convinced that Vader was on the Super Star Destroyer we were passing. He's becoming more like old Ben Kenobi every day.

We landed in a clearing of the moon's dark forest, and we soon came across a couple of Imperial scouts. One scout jumped on his speeder bike and took off, but Chewie got off a shot on his bowcaster, causing the scout to crash into a tree. Meanwhile I was in a fistfight with the other scout. Then Leia spotted two more scouts and she and Luke went after them.

When the other scout was dead, I waited in the clearing with Chewie and the droids, along with the rest of the squad. Artoo's radar screen scanned the forest. Suddenly he beeped to say that someone was coming. Next moment, Luke stepped out of the forest alone. He and Leia had been separated, so I told the squad to go ahead and meet us at the shield generator. Then Luke, Chewie, the droids and I went to look for Leia.

My heart sank into my boots when I found the charred wreckage of a speeder bike in the grass. Luke discovered two more crashed speeders, as well as Leia's helmet. Then Chewbacca scented

something and charged off through the trees. Chewie stopped when he came to a tall stake planted in the ground. There was a dead animal hanging from it. Chewie reached out to touch the meat and Luke yelled at him to stop, but he was too late. That infernal Wookiee pulled the animal from the stake and next moment we were all hanging upside down in a net, suspended high above the clearing. Artoo let out a wild series of beeps and whistles, and Chewie howled his head off. I took his paw out of my mouth and glared at him. He's always thinking with his stomach.

Artoo used his cutting tool to slice at the net, and we all tumbled to the ground. When we sat up, we were surrounded by dozens of Ewoks, each brandishing a long spear. I was getting a bad feeling, when the little Ewoks started gasping and chattering. Next thing you know, they were all bowing down in front of See-Threepio! They thought he was some sort of god.

Chewbacca and Artoo thought that was very funny, but Luke seemed to be having the same bad feeling as me, and I trust my instincts. Sure enough, fifteen minutes later we were all tied to long poles and wrapped up with vines like a bunch of cocoons. All except See-Threepio of course, who was being carried along on a litter like some kind of metallic king.

At the Ewok village, there was good news and bad news. The good news was that Leia was there, perfectly safe, and the Ewoks were putting on a banquet in See-Threepio's honour. The bad news was that we were going to be the main course.

Thankfully, we had a Jedi Knight with us. I'll never scoff at the ways of the Force again. (Well, not much.) Luke used his powers to make the Ewoks believe that See-Threepio could do magic, and after that first little bit of 'unpleasantness', we made good friends with the Ewoks. Tonight we've been telling them all about the war against the Empire, and they were so impressed that they've made us a part of the tribe. I guess short help is better than no help at all! Tomorrow, their scouts are going to show us the quickest way to the shield generator.

There was just one sour note in the proceedings this evening. I saw Luke and Leia going outside together, and after a few minutes they still hadn't come back. I went out after them, and saw Luke walking away. Leia was bathed in moonlight – she had never looked more beautiful. She was crying, and she wouldn't tell me why. Like an idiot, I lost my temper – it's like torture that she can tell things to Luke and not to me. I'm afraid, I guess – afraid that she'll choose him – and it comes out in temper. But I felt bad as I turned to walk away, and I went back to her and held her in my arms. No matter who she loves, I can't bear to see her hurt.

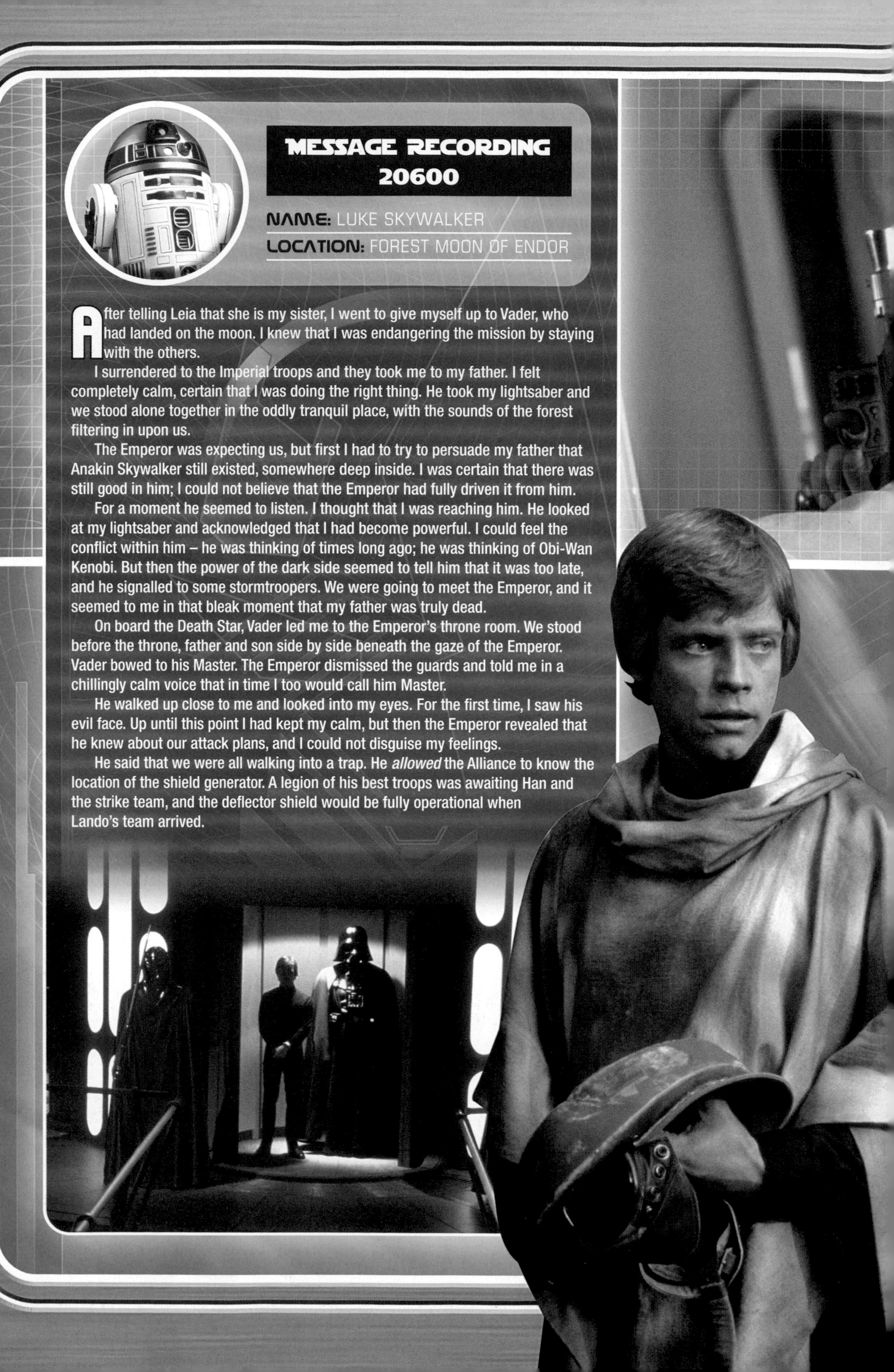

MESSAGE RECORDING 20600

NAME: LUKE SKYWALKER

LOCATION: FOREST MOON OF ENDOR

After telling Leia that she is my sister, I went to give myself up to Vader, who had landed on the moon. I knew that I was endangering the mission by staying with the others.

I surrendered to the Imperial troops and they took me to my father. I felt completely calm, certain that I was doing the right thing. He took my lightsaber and we stood alone together in the oddly tranquil place, with the sounds of the forest filtering in upon us.

The Emperor was expecting us, but first I had to try to persuade my father that Anakin Skywalker still existed, somewhere deep inside. I was certain that there was still good in him; I could not believe that the Emperor had fully driven it from him.

For a moment he seemed to listen. I thought that I was reaching him. He looked at my lightsaber and acknowledged that I had become powerful. I could feel the conflict within him – he was thinking of times long ago; he was thinking of Obi-Wan Kenobi. But then the power of the dark side seemed to tell him that it was too late, and he signalled to some stormtroopers. We were going to meet the Emperor, and it seemed to me in that bleak moment that my father was truly dead.

On board the Death Star, Vader led me to the Emperor's throne room. We stood before the throne, father and son side by side beneath the gaze of the Emperor. Vader bowed to his Master. The Emperor dismissed the guards and told me in a chillingly calm voice that in time I too would call him Master.

He walked up close to me and looked into my eyes. For the first time, I saw his evil face. Up until this point I had kept my calm, but then the Emperor revealed that he knew about our attack plans, and I could not disguise my feelings.

He said that we were all walking into a trap. He *allowed* the Alliance to know the location of the shield generator. A legion of his best troops was awaiting Han and the strike team, and the deflector shield would be fully operational when Lando's team arrived.

MESSAGE RECORDING 20601

NAME: HAN SOLO

LOCATION: FOREST MOON OF ENDOR

Early the next day, we were on a ridge overlooking the shield generator. The main entrance to the bunker was on the far side of the landing platform. It wasn't going to be easy, but I knew we could do it. With the help of our new Ewok furball friends, we got past the Imperial scouts and entered the bunker, leaving the droids outside on guard duty. There was no sign of life inside. We crept towards the main control room and herded all the workers away from the control panels. We had to work fast – our fleet was due to arrive at any moment.

I was just setting the charges when a voice told us to freeze. We spun around and saw dozens of Imperial weapons trained on us. Imperial troops poured into the room, disarming us and taking control. We were helpless.

MESSAGE RECORDING 20602

NAME: LANDO CALRISSIAN

LOCATION: FOREST MOON OF ENDOR

I made a final check of the fleet, asking all wings to report in. I knew that Admiral Ackbar was watching the fighters massing from the bridge of the Rebel headquarters frigate. At last Admiral Ackbar gave the order and we jumped to hyperspace.

As we drew near to the Death Star, I was worried; we couldn't get a reading on whether the shield was up or down. That information can be jammed, but how could they be jamming us if they didn't know that we were coming? It didn't make sense. The shield must still be up! I couldn't risk it – I gave the order to break off the attack and we all veered off desperately to avoid the unseen wall.

Seconds later, we spotted enemy ships in sector 47 – the massive Imperial fleet was waiting for us! We headed straight into an armada of TIE fighters. The sky exploded into light and flame as a fierce dogfight began. We accelerated to attack speed – we had to draw their fire away from our cruisers!

MESSAGE RECORDING 20603

NAME: LUKE SKYWALKER

LOCATION: FOREST MOON OF ENDOR

From the window of the Emperor's throne room, I could see the distant flashes of the space battle. The Emperor began to taunt me, urging me to use the hate that was swelling in me. He was right – I could feel it growing as he laughed at our failure, as I imagined my friends dying.

As another Rebel ship exploded against the protective shield of the Death Star, the Emperor pressed on with his cold mockery, telling me that my friends had failed. Then he issued an order into his comlink, and the Death Star fired on a Rebel cruiser, blowing it to smithereens. The Death Star was fully operational!

MESSAGE RECORDING 20604

NAME: LANDO CALRISSIAN

LOCATION: FOREST MOON OF ENDOR

Ackbar wanted to retreat, but I knew we wouldn't get another chance at this. I was sure that Han would get the shield down – we just had to give him more time. I gave the order to move in closer and engage the Star Destroyers at point-blank range. We would last longer against them than we would against the Death Star – and we might just take a few of them with us.

MESSAGE RECORDING 20605

NAME: PRINCESS LEIA

LOCATION: FOREST MOON OF ENDOR

We were led out of the bunker and for a while it seemed as if the Empire had won. But they had reckoned without the brave little Ewoks! Hundreds of Ewoks threw their furry bodies into the fray against the stormtroopers and their walkers. That was when Chewie turned up – in the cockpit of an Imperial walker! The giant machine blasted the doors off the bunker and Han was able to destroy the generator. The shield was down and our fighters could attack!

MESSAGE RECORDING 20606

NAME: LUKE SKYWALKER

LOCATION: FOREST MOON OF ENDOR

Outside, the Rebel fleet was being decimated and inside the Emperor was getting inside my head like a disease. I could no longer hold in my rage – I grabbed my lightsaber and began to battle Vader. It was a vicious duel and I knocked Vader backwards, but then I realised that I was using the dark side. My father's thoughts were betraying him – I could feel the good in him, the conflict. I could not fight him. However, he sensed my feelings for my sister and used them against me, enraging me again. This time I knocked him to his knees and slashed his hand off at the wrist, holding my blade at his throat. The Emperor, unable to control his excitement, urged me to kill my father.

At that moment I realised how much I was becoming like my father. I stepped back and threw my lightsaber away from me. I would never turn to the dark side. Enraged, the Emperor shot blinding bolts of Force lightning – evil energy – straight at me. I shrank before them, my knees buckling. Vader stood and watched as I writhed in agony and begged him to help me.

My father grabbed the Emperor from behind and lifted him high into the air, away from me. The white lightning struck him and he stumbled as the sparks rained off his helmet and flew down over his black cape. He held his evil Master high over his head and walked to the edge of the abyss at the central core of the throne room. With one final burst of strength, he hurled the Emperor's body into the bottomless shaft. The Emperor's body spun helplessly into the void and exploded. My father collapsed, and I pulled him away from the edge of the abyss.

At that moment, three X-wings were leading the way into the Death Star shaft, followed by the *Falcon* and four other fighters. Outside, our fighters blew up a Super Star Destroyer! The Death Star was rocked by explosions. In the midst of this uproar, I was trying to carry my father's body towards an Imperial shuttle. Finally, my father asked me to take his mask off.

Beneath the black mask was the terribly scarred face of an old man. He smiled at me . . . and died. In the end, my father the Jedi Knight had returned – and saved the galaxy.

I dragged his body towards a shuttle as a huge explosion rocked the docking bay. In the *Millennium Falcon*, Lando was leading a bomb run through the structure of the Death Star and chain-reaction explosions were destroying the evil weapon. Finally, they fired their missiles at the centre of the main reactor – just as I was rocketing out of the main docking bay.

Our greatest battle is over, and we have won. Han and my sister are in love, all misunderstandings cleared away. Everywhere are wild celebrations of victory and liberation. Our little group of adventurers is still together, and we are joined by the shimmering figures of those who have gone before us and become part of the living Force – Master Yoda, Obi-Wan Kenobi . . . and Anakin Skywalker.

Skywalker

Gredda and Lef Lars

Edern Lars

Aika Lars

Cliegg Lars

Shmi Skywalker

(first marriage)

(second marriage)

Beru Whitesun

Owen Lars

Bail Organa

Queen Breha Organa

Anakin Skywalker

(adopted)

Han Solo

Princess Leia Organa

Jacen Solo

Jaina Solo

Anakin Solo

(adopted)

Family Tree

Ryoo
(Sola's maternal grandmother)

Winama

Pooja
(Darred's maternal grandmother)

Jobal Naberrie

Ruwee Naberrie

Padmé Amidala
(Padmé Naberrie)

Sola Naberrie

Darred Janren Naberrie

Pooja
Naberrie

Ryoo
Naberrie

Luke Skywalker

Mara Jade
Skywalker

Ben Skywalker

QUIZ
Part Six

ANSWER THESE QUESTIONS ABOUT THE END OF THE EMPIRE AND ADD YOUR SCORE TO YOUR TOTAL FROM PARTS 1–5 TO GET YOUR FINAL TOTAL. THEN FIND OUT HOW KNOWLEDGEABLE YOU REALLY ARE, AND WHAT YOUR ABILITIES SAY ABOUT YOUR DESTINY.

QUESTION 1

What was the name of the dancer slave girl whom Jabba the Hutt fed to the Rancor?

Oola

QUESTION 2

Who caused Boba Fett to fall into the Pit of Carkoon?

Han Solo

QUESTION 3

Who was Boussh?

Princess Leia

QUESTION 4

Who was Lando's co-pilot during the Battle of Endor?

Nien Numb

QUESTION 5

Where did Luke surrender to the Imperial troops?

Forest moon of Endor

QUESTION 6

Who was the leader of the Rebel Alliance?

Mon Mothma

QUESTION 7

Where did Luke hide his lightsaber when he went to bargain for Han's life with Jabba the Hutt?

inside R2-D2

QUESTION 8

What offer did the Emperor make to Luke?

To take Darth vader's place at his side

QUESTION 9

Which ship fired the final, fatal missile on the Death Star?

Millium Falcon

QUESTION 10

Which Ewok did Leia meet first?

Wicket

PART 6 SCORE

10 out of **10**

RESULTS

60 – A perfect score! You must have studied hard – and with your powers of concentration and excellent memory, you would make a powerful Jedi Master.

51–59 – A highly respectable score. Like a new Jedi Knight, you have achieved great things, but you cannot afford to be complacent. You have many lessons still to learn.

21–50 – A good try, but you still have a long way to go. Your powers of recall and attention put you at the level of Padawan.

0–20 – A shamefully low score. You must pay attention to detail if you are to become strong in the Force.

ANSWERS

QUIZ PART 1

1. Nute Gunray
2. He crashed Boss Nass's heyblibber
3. Naberrie
4. Watto
5. Anakin Skywalker
6. Senator Palpatine
7. Captain Panaka
8. Queen Amidala
9. Darth Maul
10. Gungan

QUIZ PART 2

1. Cordé
2. Jar Jar Binks
3. Dexter Jettster
4. Revenge – they killed his mother
5. Sola
6. His mother
7. Nexu, Orray, Reek, Acklay
8. Darth Tyranus
9. R2-D2 and C-3PO
10. A droid army

QUIZ PART 3

1. Three
2. Four
3. Anakin Skywalker
4. Bail Organa
5. Nine – the business on Cato Nemoidia didn't count
6. Utapau
7. Mace Windu
8. To kill all the Jedi in the Temple
9. She died of a broken heart
10. Captain Antilles

QUIZ PART 4

1. Shmi Skywalker
2. Red Five
3. Greedo
4. *Millennium Falcon*
5. Obi-Wan Kenobi
6. Dantooine
7. Biggs Darklighter
8. Pull their arms out of their sockets
9. Obi-Wan Kenobi
10. For luck

QUIZ PART 5

1. Wampa
2. *Millennium Falcon*
3. Because Obi-Wan told him that Master Yoda was waiting there to train him in the ways of the Jedi
4. Mynock
5. A vision of Darth Vader
6. C-3PO
7. None
8. 'I know'
9. Boba Fett
10. Tatooine

QUIZ PART 6

1. Oola
2. Han Solo
3. Princess Leia
4. Nien Nunb
5. Forest moon of Endor
6. Mon Mothma
7. Inside R2-D2
8. To take Darth Vader's place at his side
9. *Millennium Falcon*
10. Wicket